Using Statistics

James Reilly

Gill & Macmillan

Gill & Macmillan
Hume Avenue
Park West
Dublin 12
with associated companies throughout the world
www.gillmacmillan.ie

ISBN-13: 978 07171 40220
ISBN-10: 0 7171 4022 9

Index compiled by Cover to Cover
Print origination in Ireland by O'K Graphic Design, Dublin

The paper used in this book is made from the wood pulp of managed forests. For every tree felled, at least one is planted, thereby renewing natural resources.

A catalogue record is available for this book from the British Library.

Table of Contents

To Joanie – unique, courageous, beloved

Acknowledgments

I wish to thank:

My students, some of whose projects are featured in these pages; my work colleagues and clients; Noel Raftery, my first mentor in statistical process control; Minitab Inc., for the use of MINITAB statistical software; the staff at Gill & Macmillan, especially Marion O'Brien, Seamus Gorman, Aoileann O'Donnell, Emma Farrell, Linda Murphy and Louise Callaghan; my mother and father, who have been two strong pillars in my life.

Support Material for

USING STATISTICS

Dynamic and easy to use, online support material for this book

provides lecturers with:

- PowerPoint slides
- Various web links
- Data sets for each chapter, which support all statistical software.

To access Lecturer support material on our secure site

1) Go to www.gillmacmillan.ie/lecturers
2) Logon using your username and password. If you don't have a password, register online and we will email your password to you.

provides students with:

- Web links
- Data sets for each chapter, which support all statistical software.

To access Student support material

1) Go to www.gillmacmillan.ie/student
2) Click on the link for Student Support material

1

OBSERVATION

At the end of this chapter you will be able to:

- construct and interpret graphs and data summaries;
- draw samples and make inferences.

Statistics allows numbers to talk. The numbers tell a story. This story can provide information that will help us to reach verdicts and make decisions. We could say that statistics delivers insight that provides confidence and leads to action.

Stories may contain a lot of trivial details. We need to avoid getting swamped in these details, and stand back to see the big picture. When exploring a set of data, a **histogram** can provide a bird's eye view.

Graphs

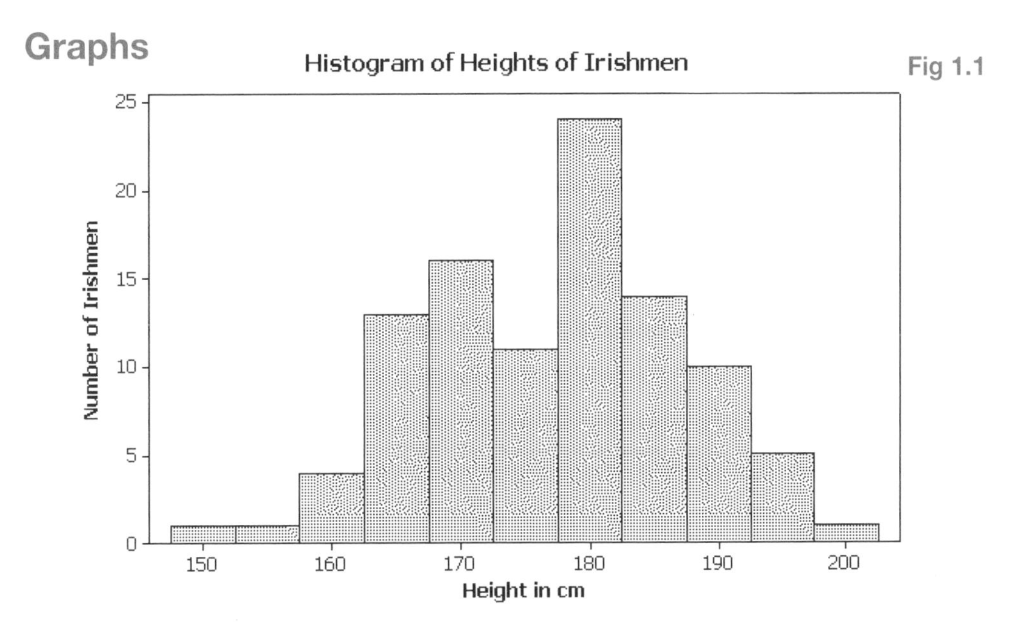

Fig 1.1

When reading a histogram, focus on the shape rather than the numbers. Also, ignore small irregularities and pay attention to the more important features. Therefore, when you look at the histogram above you should see the **frequency curve** below. There is no need to draw the frequency curve – you should be able to see it in your mind's eye.

Fig 1.2

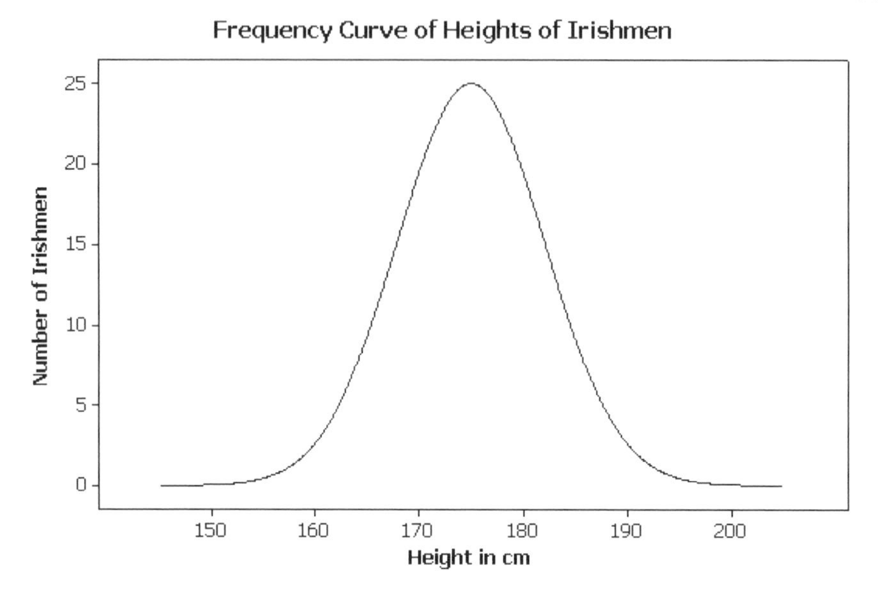

Question: What story is this histogram telling?
Answer: There is a typical height that is common, and while some people are taller or shorter than this, very tall and very short people are rare.

We can tell all this by noting the peak in the middle, and the tails on either side. This bell-shaped pattern is very common and is referred to as **normal**. Also, notice that we told the story without quoting any numbers. We allowed the numbers to talk.

What other patterns might arise? Here are some.

Fig 1.3

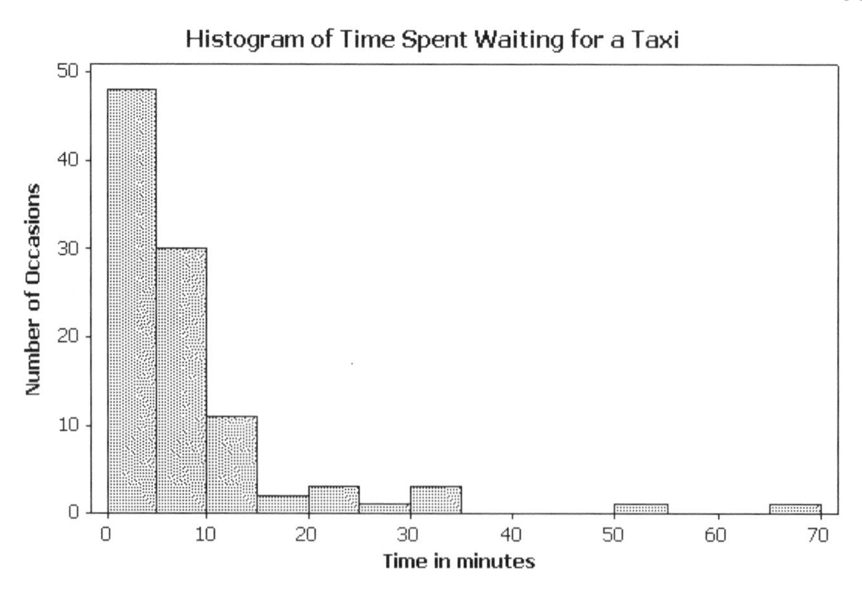

Fig 1.4

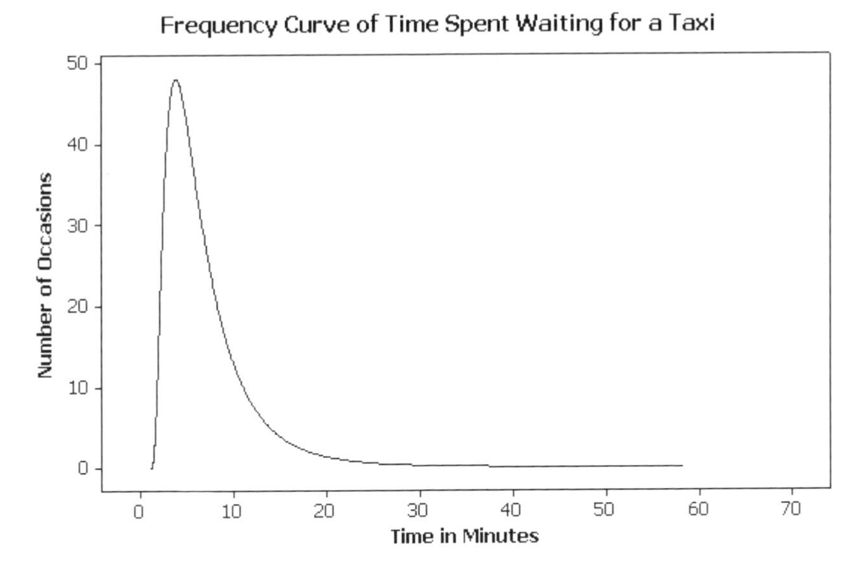

The difference here is that the tails are not symmetric. We say that these data are positively **skewed**, or skewed to the right. The waiting time for a taxi might be much longer than expected, but could not be much shorter than expected, because the waiting time cannot be less than zero.

Fig 1.5

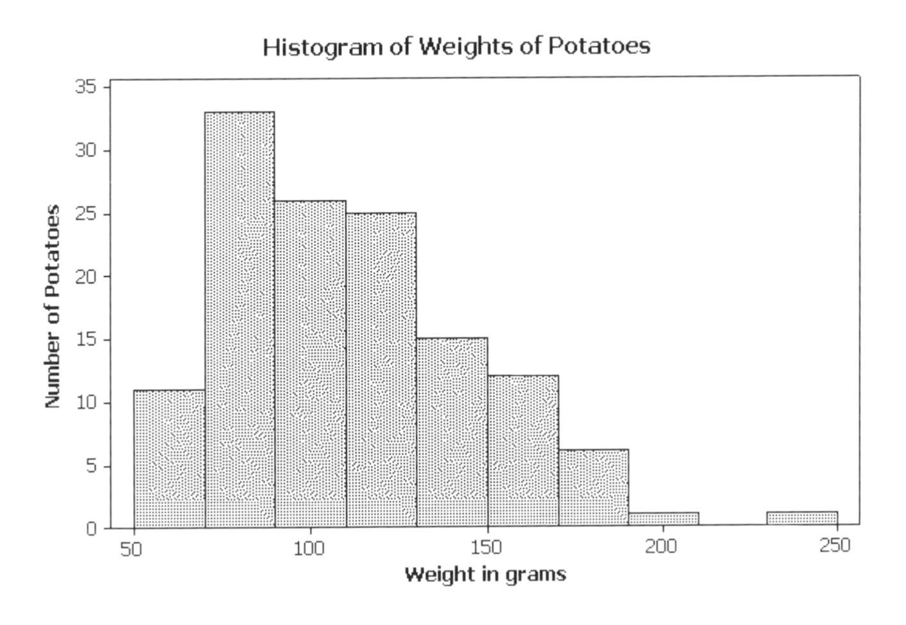

Fig 1.6

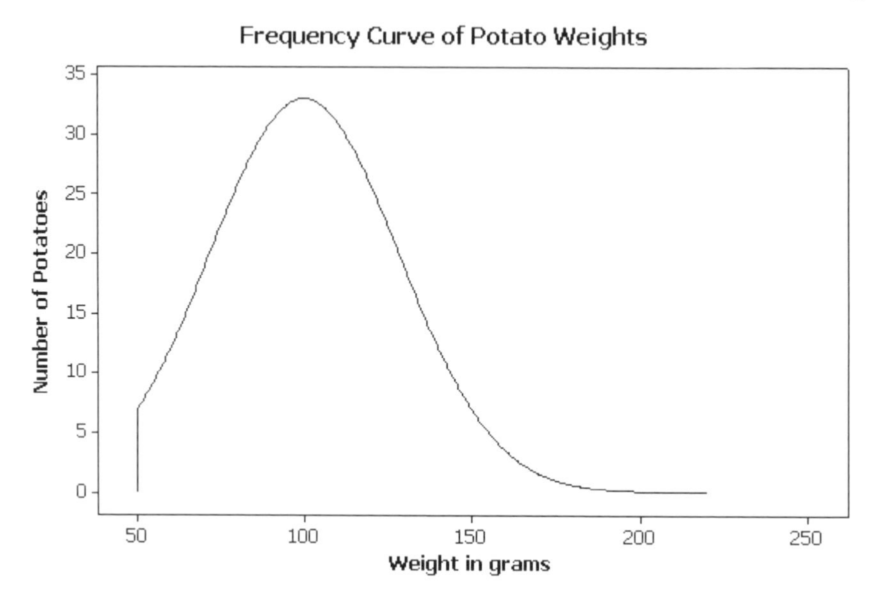

Can you tell by looking at the histogram that these potatoes come from a supermarket and not from a farm? The potatoes have been sorted, and any potato weighing less than 50 grams has been removed. We say that the frequency curve is **truncated**. A frequency curve can be truncated on the left, or on the right, or on both sides.

Fig 1.7

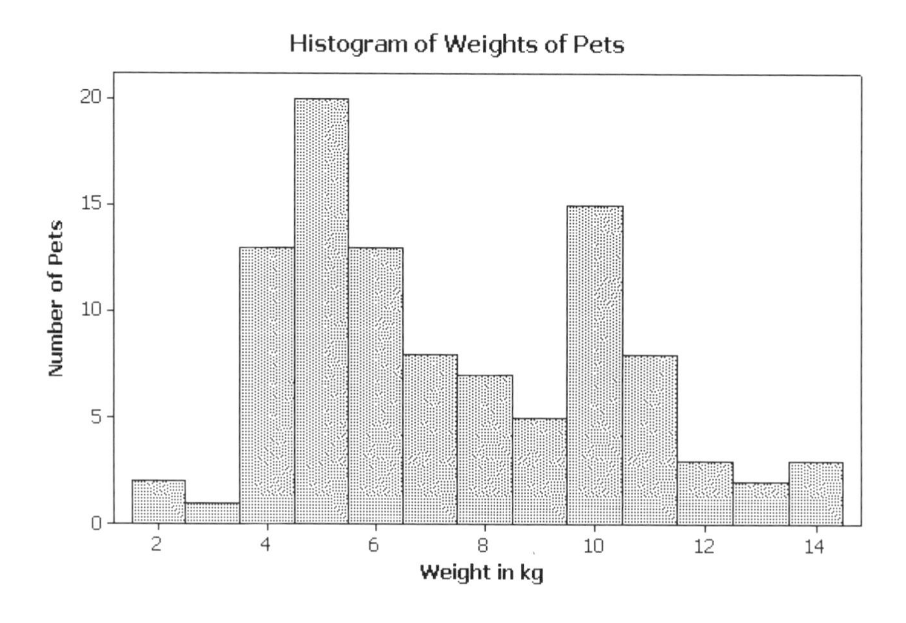

Fig 1.8

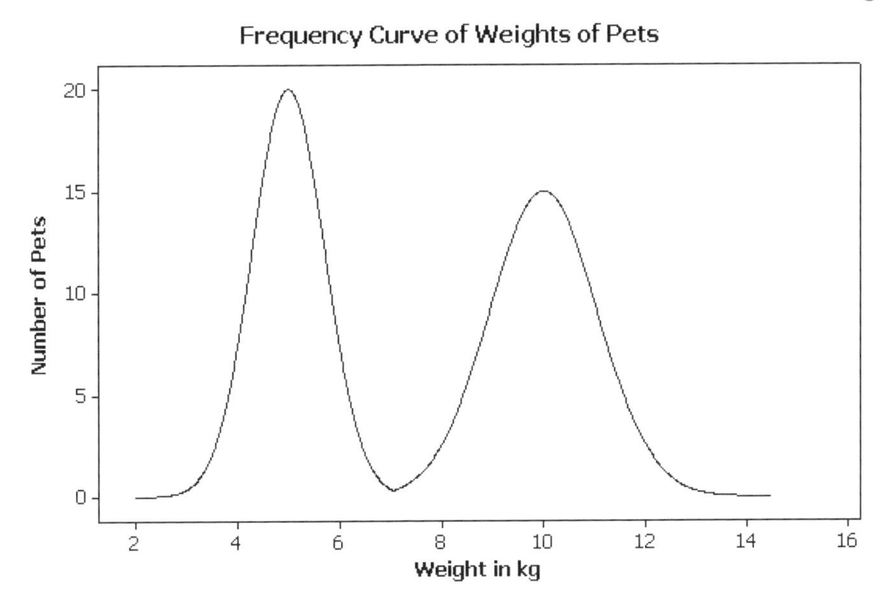

Although these animals are all called pets, we can see from the histogram that they are not a homogeneous group. Maybe there is a mixture of cats and dogs. We say that these data are **bimodal**, because instead of having one common value (**mode**) we have two.

Fig 1.9

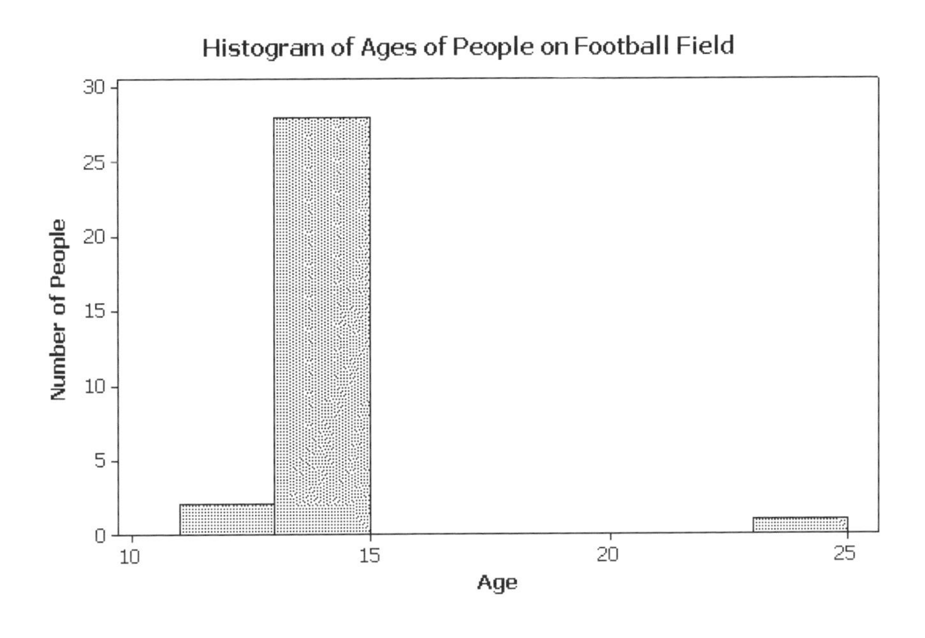

Fig 1.10

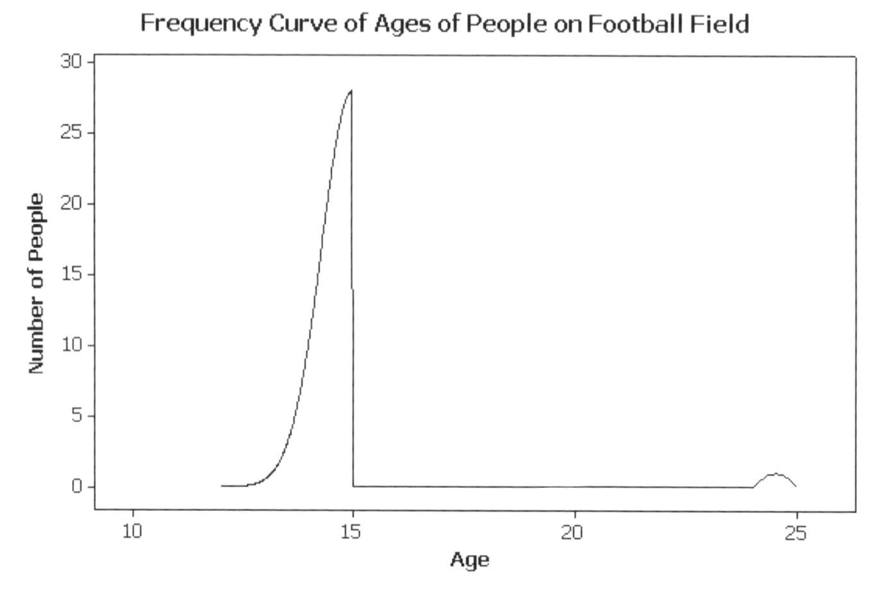

One of these numbers does not seem to belong with the rest. It is called an **outlier**. Outliers may represent the most interesting feature of the data set. On the other hand, they may simply be the result of someone making a mistake when typing the numbers. What do you think the outlier represents in the histogram above?

Organising Data

A software package will accept the **raw data**, and draw a histogram for you. To draw a histogram by hand, you will first need to organise the data into a **frequency table**. The raw data below represent morning journey times in minutes for a certain commuter.

40, 42, 51, 96, 62, 46, 61, 44, 71, 51, 42, 59, 47, 47, 52, 53, 49,
44, 84, 83, 45, 45, 54, 41, 44, 48, 44, 76, 61, 42, 51, 74, 66, 47,
76, 47, 52, 41, 50, 42, 55, 40, 77, 50, 43, 45, 48, 44, 70, 47, 44,
55, 57, 95, 51, 50, 51, 88, 53, 65, 57, 48, 62, 53, 42, 45, 70, 57,
44, 43, 40, 71, 58, 72, 53, 43, 43, 52, 49, 44, 63, 44, 47, 48, 47,
46, 41, 64, 77, 48, 42, 40, 70, 65, 42, 41, 40, 40, 50, 68

Follow the steps below to produce a frequency table.

1. Identify the maximum and the minimum values, i.e. 96 and 40.
2. Calculate the range: maximum – minimum, i.e. 96 – 40 = 56.

3. Divide the range by 10 to suggest the class interval, i.e. 56/10 = 5.6, so intervals 5 units wide would be OK.
4. Create about ten, non-overlapping, classes, i.e. 40 to 44 inclusive, 45 to 49, 50 to 54, etc.
5. Make a **tally sheet** as shown below, and fill in the first column.
6. Now, read through the data once only, making a mark in the second column for each **datum** (singular of 'data') in the appropriate row of the tally sheet. Only the first four tally marks are shown.

Table 1.1

Journey Time (X)	Tally	Frequency (f)
40 to 44	//	
45 to 49		
50 to 54	/	
55 to 59		
60 to 64		
65 to 69		
70 to 74		
75 to 79		
80 to 84		
85 to 89		
90 to 94		
95 to 99	/	

7. When you have completed the tally, tot up the tally marks in each class and enter the result in the frequency column.
   The completed frequency table is shown below.

Table 1.2

Journey Time (X)	Frequency (f)
40 to 44	30
45 to 49	20
50 to 54	17
55 to 59	7
60 to 64	6
65 to 69	4
70 to 74	7
75 to 79	4
80 to 84	2
85 to 89	1
90 to 94	0
95 to 99	2

Now you are ready to draw a histogram. The variable (**X**) goes on the horizontal axis, and the frequency (**f**) goes on the vertical axis.

Every graph you draw should have the following features:

1. A title that immediately tells what the graph is about.
2. Sensible text labels on both axes – not just '**X**' and '**f**'.
3. Units on both axes. The frequency axis should begin at zero, but the **X**-axis should begin at the minimum value. Do not try to cram in all the numbers: a few **tick-marks** look better.
4. If appropriate, include a footnote to indicate the source of the data.

Fig 1.11

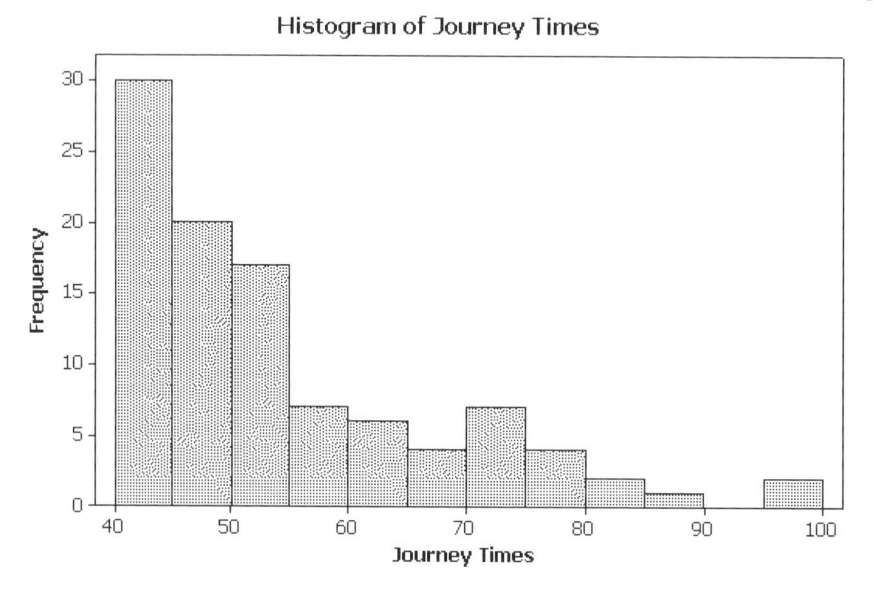

The histogram indicates that, under ideal conditions, the journey can be completed in about 40 minutes. Adverse traffic conditions may substantially increase the journey time.

Time Series Plots

A **time series plot** is useful for showing how a variable behaves over time. Time is represented on the horizontal axis, and the variable in question is represented on the vertical axis. Each observation is plotted as a point, and these points are joined together with line segments. Time series plots of sales figures, manufacturing measurements, air temperature, and many other variables, are common. When you scan a time series plot with your eyes, remember that time progresses from left to right, and we wish to see whether the figures remain steady, rise or fall suddenly, rise or fall gradually, follow repetitive cycles, or display some other pattern. Some typical time series patterns are illustrated below. These examples are based on the daily revenue of a number of different businesses.

Fig 1.12

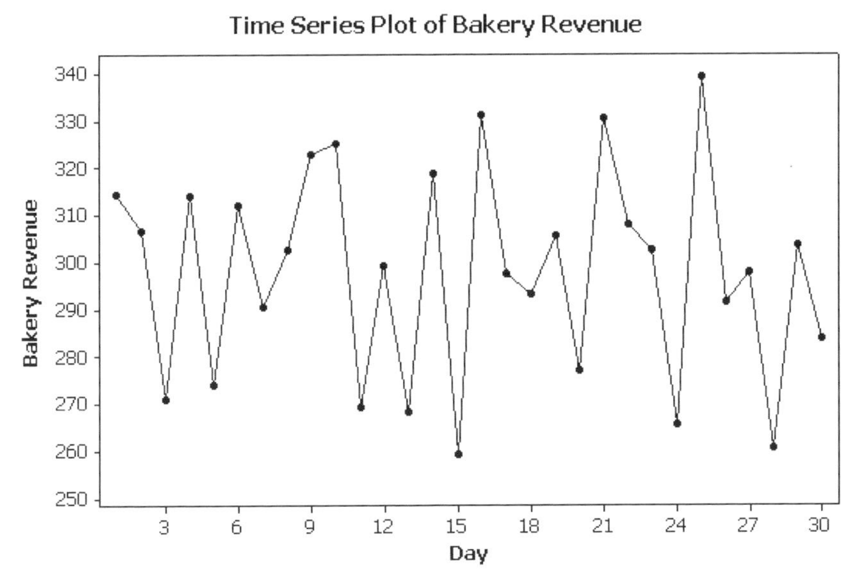

In the first time series plot above, there is a good deal of random variation, but there is no obvious pattern. We conclude that the variable remained more or less steady throughout the period. This is the most common kind of time series plot, and it corresponds to a normal frequency curve. If the graph was rotated anti-clockwise through 90 degrees, and the points fell onto the variable axis, they would form a bell-shaped mound.

Fig 1.13

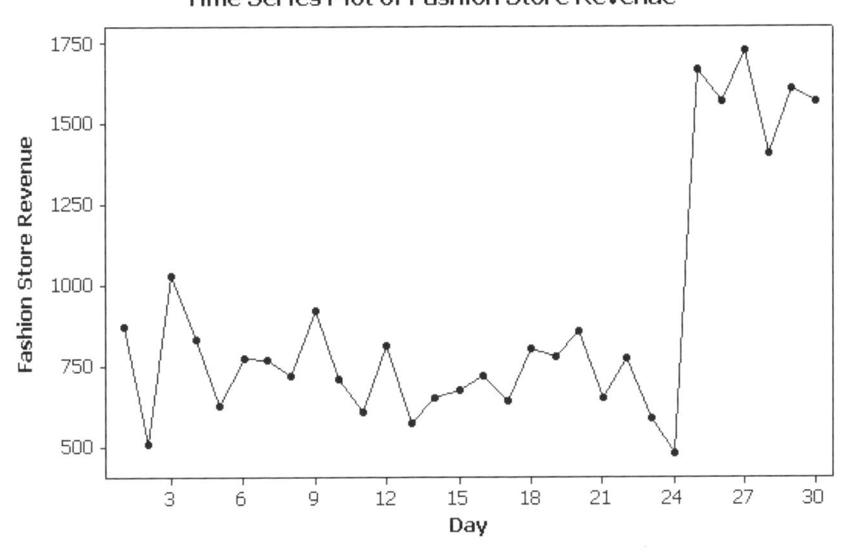

The striking feature of the second time series plot is the **shift**, i.e. the sudden change in the figures. There must be some explanation for this – perhaps a sale began.

Fig 1.14

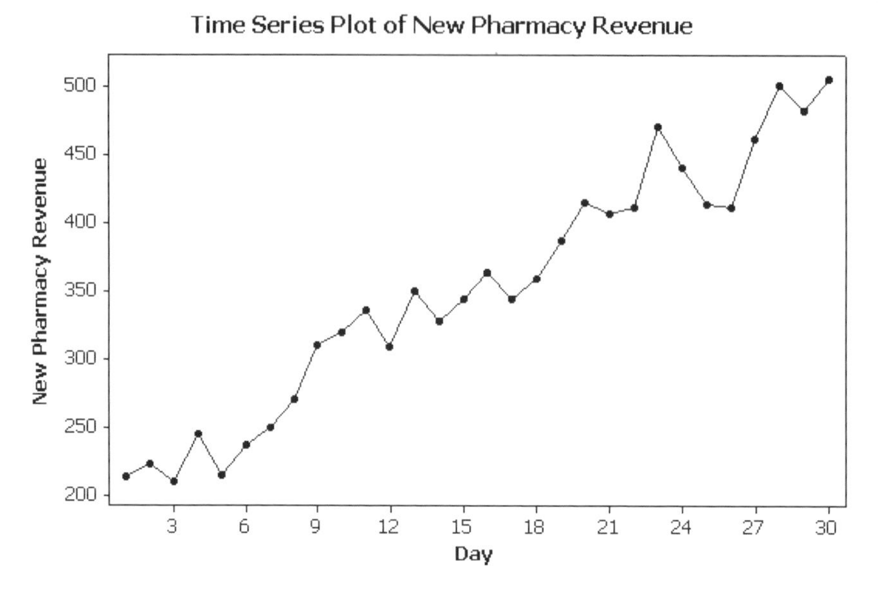

A new pharmacy has opened recently. The time series plot of daily revenue shows a **trend**, i.e. a gradual movement in the figures. As the new pharmacy becomes known, its customers increase in number. Because there is some random variation present, this trend may not be obvious until we view the graph.

Fig 1.15

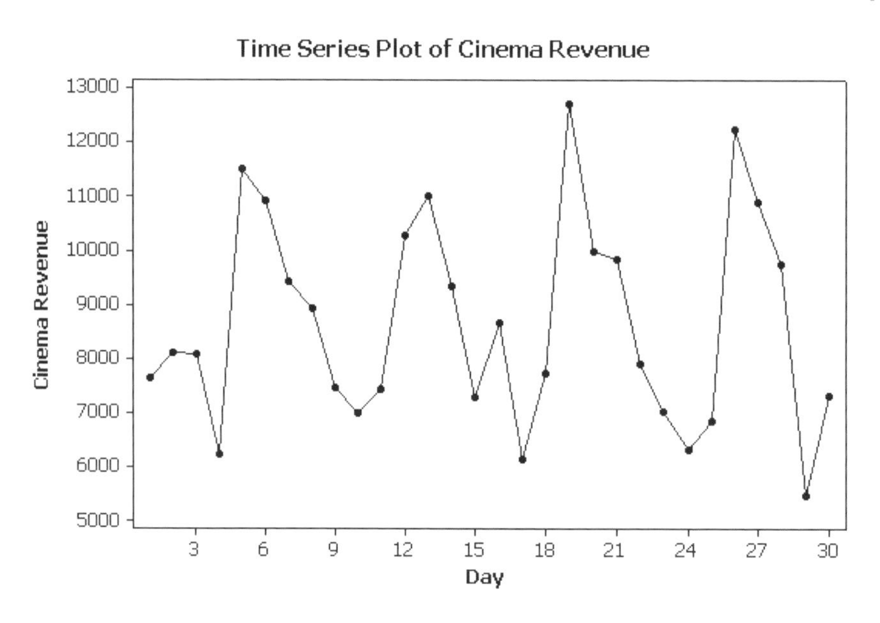

The final plot shows an obvious **cyclical** pattern. Cinemas are busier at weekends. The word cyclical can be replaced by the word **seasonal** when the cycle in question is of one year's duration.

Histograms and time series plots are two powerful techniques for exploring data. When a histogram shows a non-normal pattern, or a time series displays a non-random scatter of points, then the data have a story to tell. The ability to interpret the story requires a knowledge of the relevant professional area (finance, biology, engineering or whatever), as well as a knowledge of statistics.

Problems 1.1

1. For each of the following variables, would you expect a histogram to be normal, skewed, truncated or bimodal? Explain your answers.
   (a) The heights of adults.
   (b) The volumes of sauce in bottles that contain a nominal 500 g.
   (c) The amounts of landline telephone bills for residential customers.
   (d) The times between callers to a library.
   (e) The nightly attendances at a pantomime.
   (f) The widths of leaves on a sycamore tree.
   (g) The ages of spectators at an inter-schools debate.
2. For each of the following variables, describe three different scenarios in each case that could result in a time series plot exhibiting a shift, a trend or a cyclical pattern.
   (a) Air temperature in a classroom over the course of a day.
   (b) Daily attendance at lectures over the course of a term.
   (c) Monthly electricity consumption in a small town over the course of a decade.
3. The data below represent the transaction amounts, in euro, at a forecourt shop. Use a histogram to obtain some insight into the character of this business. (Note: All data sets in this book are available at http://www.gillmacmillan.ie, so you can use software to solve all the problems, if you wish.)

   43.24, 17.89, 51.68, 43.00, 2.81, 1.94, 4.26, 0.98, 26.74, 32.00, 46.00, 45.90, 43.00, 6.39, 50.95, 37.00, 46.03, 20.37, 50.00, 21.46, 3.16, 2.24, 46.02, 3.38, 53.00, 21.00, 2.83, 49.16, 3.81, 3.87, 12.41, 38.93, 23.46, 34.00, 45.79, 3.16, 4.88, 4.36, 48.00, 34.11, 41.00, 2.20, 1.92, 44.00, 47.37, 41.00, 32.78, 48.00, 2.63, 31.72, 2.98, 2.28, 27.00, 42.00, 22.37, 28.00, 48.63, 38.00, 3.11, 33.00, 45.00, 3.84, 0.97, 28.58, 32.01, 32.00, 26.00, 31.20, 38.00, 2.23, 38.90, 35.00, 3.11, 35.00, 33.00, 1.86, 4.33, 34.00, 1.74, 37.93, 55.00, 29.00, 34.00, 52.35, 35.00, 13.01, 48.00, 32.00, 4.18, 38.00, 50.00, 32.00, 42.00, 51.00, 46.00, 40.00, 2.50, 28.18, 3.44, 44.00

4. The individual weights, in mg, of tablets in a consignment are shown below. With the help of a histogram, what can you say about the pharmaceutical production and inspection processes?

   408, 404, 405, 409, 409, 407, 404, 404, 407, 407, 407, 407, 407, 410, 407, 409, 409, 410, 407, 409, 406, 407, 406, 410, 405, 407, 409, 409, 405, 404, 409, 405, 407, 408, 410, 408, 406, 405, 407, 406, 405, 405, 406, 401, 408, 406, 409, 406, 404, 406, 405, 406, 407, 410, 407, 408, 405, 408, 410, 407, 405, 405, 405, 407, 409, 403, 405, 408, 408, 407, 406, 403, 406, 410, 405, 402, 409, 407, 402, 404, 410, 408, 408, 402, 409, 408, 405, 409, 404, 408, 404, 405, 408, 406, 410, 408, 406, 407, 408, 405

Sampling

We now come to a very important and surprising concept. The data that we collect and analyse are not the data that we are interested in! Usually we are interested in a much larger data set, one which is simply too big to collect. The **population** is the name given to the complete data set of interest. The population must be clearly defined at the beginning of an investigation, e.g. the shoe-sizes of all the people who live in Galway. Note that a population is not a set of people but a set of numbers, and we will never see most of these numbers.

Sometimes the measurements of interest arise in connection with some **process**, e.g. the dissolution times in water of a certain new tablet. In this case there is no population out there to begin with: we must make some of the tablets and dissolve them in water, or else there is nothing to measure. Also, the process could be repeated any number of times in the future, so the population is infinitely large.

Once a tablet has been dissolved, it cannot be sold or used again. This is an example of a **destructive measurement**. This is another reason why we cannot measure everything that interests us: we would have plenty of data, but no merchandise left to sell.

We have seen that we virtually never take a **census** of every unit in the population. Instead we collect a **sample** from the population and we assume that the other data in the population are similar to the data in the sample. We see only a part, but we imagine what the complete picture looks like. This kind of reasoning is called **inference**.

Because we use a sample to provide information about a population, it is essential that the sample is **representative**. The sample may not give perfect information, but it should not be misleading. **Bias** occurs if the sample is selected or used in such a way that it gives a one-sided view of the population.

Sampling Techniques

Random Sampling

A simple random sample is a sample selected in such a way that every unit in the population has an equal chance of being selected.

If the population is finite, this can be done by assigning identification numbers, from 1 to **N**, to all the units in the population, and then using the random number generator on your calculator to select units using the formula below.

Formula 1.1

> **Random Sampling**
>
> $i = INT(N.X+1)$
>
> identifies number '**i**' at random from among the numbers 1,2 … **N**, where **X** is a uniform random number in the range (0,1).

Example: Select two letters at random from the alphabet.

First, assign an ID to each letter. Let A=1, B=2, etc. The identification numbers can often be assigned by using the order of arrival, or the positions, of the units. Next, generate two random numbers: say, 0.933 and 0.687.

N = 26

i = INT(26 × 0.933 + 1) = INT(25.258) = 25, the letter 'Y'

i = INT(26 × 0.687 + 1) = INT(18.862) = 18, the letter 'R'

This approach allows sampling with **replacement**, but repeats can be disallowed if sampling without replacement is preferred.

If a population is infinite, or diffuse, it can be impossible to assign identification numbers. Suppose we wish to interview a random sample of 100 shoppers at a mall. It is not feasible to assign a number to each shopper, and we cannot compel any shopper to be interviewed. We have no choice but to interview willing shoppers 'here and there' in the mall, and hope that the sample is representative. However, when such informal sampling techniques are used, there is always the possibility of bias in the sample. For example, busy shoppers will not be inclined to complete questionnaires, but if our survey asks 'Have you ever purchased a microwavable dinner?' then such people would be more likely to answer 'yes' than the people who are sampled.

Stratified Sampling

Let us suppose that we plan to open a hairdressing business in Kilkenny. We might decide to interview a random sample of adults in the city to investigate their frequency of visits to the hairdresser. If our sample just happened to include a large majority of women, then the results could be misleading. It makes better sense to first divide the population of adults into two strata, men and women, and then to draw a random sample from each stratum.

Cluster Sampling

It is tempting to select naturally occurring clusters of units, rather than the units themselves. For example, we might wish to study the tread on the tyres of cars passing along a certain road. If we randomly select 25 cars and check all four tyres on each car, this is not equivalent to a random sample of 100 tyres. All the tyres on the same car may have similar tread. The selected units are random, but not independently random. If the units of interest are tyres, then select tyres, not cars.

Quota Sampling

Quota sampling is also called **convenience sampling**. With this approach, it does not matter how the data are collected so long as the sample size is reached. Usually the first units are selected because this is the easiest thing to do. But systematic variation in the population may mean that the first units are not representative of the rest of the population – people who are first to purchase a product, fruit at the top of a box, calls made early in the morning, etc.

Systematic Sampling

With this approach, units are selected at regular intervals. For example, every tenth box from a packing operation is inspected for packing defects. But suppose there are two packers, Clodagh and Mignon, who take turns packing the boxes. Then, if the first box inspected (box 1) is Clodagh's, the next box inspected (box 11) will be Clodagh's, and so on. Mignon's boxes are never inspected! All of Mignon's boxes might be incorrectly packed, but the sample indicates that everything is fine. The problem here is that the sampling interval can easily correspond to some periodic variation in the population itself.

In summary, only random samples can be relied upon to be free from bias. Random samples avoid biases due to systematic or periodic variation in the population, or due to personal biases, whether conscious or unconscious. Data collection is crucial and it must be done carefully and honestly. All the formulae in this book are based on the assumptions that random sampling has been employed and that the population is infinitely large. If samples are drawn by any technique that is not strictly random, then keep your eyes open for any potential sources of bias.

Types of Data

Information comes in two forms: numbers and text.

Question: How many minutes long was the movie? **Answer**: 115 (a number).

Question: What did you eat at the movie? **Answer**: Popcorn (text).

The second question can be re-phrased to invite a simple 'yes or no' answer.

Question: Did you eat popcorn at the movie? **Answer**: Yes (yes or no).

The two types of data, which we have described here as numbers and text, are called **measurements** and **attributes** respectively. A measurement is said to be **continuous** if any value within a given range could arise, e.g. your height could be 1.5 m or 2 m or anything in between. A measurement is said to be **discrete** if only certain values are possible, e.g. your shoe size could be 6 or 6.5, but cannot be anything in between. In the case of measurement data we will often use the **mean** to express how big the measurements are.

Attribute data are called **binary** if there are only two categories (yes and no) and are called **nominal** if there are more than two categories (popcorn, chocolate, ice-cream). It is sometimes convenient to convert binary data into numbers by means of an **indicator variable** that designates 'yes' as 1 and 'no' as 0. In the case of attribute data we will often use the **proportion** to express how common the attribute is.

PROBLEMS 1.2

1. Identify one potential source of bias in each of the following sampling schemes:
   (a) The first 50 passengers who boarded a train were asked if they were satisfied with the train timetable.
   (b) An interviewer was instructed to interview any 20 dog owners and find out if their dog had ever bitten anyone.
   (c) An agricultural laboratory requested a farmer to provide ten stalks of wheat for analysis. The farmer pulled a handful of ten stalks from the edge of the field.
   (d) In a study into the lengths of words used in newspapers, an investigator recorded the number of letters in the first word on every page.
2. Use a random number generator to select three names from the following list: Mirabelle, Kaitlin, Sarah, Toni, Emie, Grace, Kim, Iona, Stephanie.

Summary Statistics

In a conversation or in a written message, long lists of numbers are not helpful. It is better to mention a single number. A single number is easier to remember, easier to base a decision upon, and easier to compare with some other situation. For these reasons, we now consider **summary statistics**. A **statistic** is any quantity which is calculated from sample data, such as the minimum, the mean, etc. A statistic that summarises the information contained in the sample is called a summary statistic.

Example: The heights in metres of a random sample of trees in a forest were as follows.
2, 8, 5, 2, 3.

The **mean** of this sample is 4. This is an **average** or a **measure of location**, because it tells where the numbers are located on the number line. It tells us typically how big the trees are. The mean is the sum of the numbers divided by the number of numbers. It is the most popular measure of location because it takes all the sample data into account, and it is well suited to data that are roughly equal. The mean is also called the **expected value**. The sample mean is called 'X bar' and its formula is shown below.

Formula 1.2

Sample Mean (Raw Data)

$$\bar{X} = \frac{\sum X}{n}$$

Formula 1.3

Sample Mean (Frequency Data)

$$\bar{X} = \frac{\sum fX}{\sum f}$$

There are many other summary measures of location, and we describe two of them here: the mode and the median. The **mode** is the most commonly occurring value and it is useful if the data are nearly all the same. To the question 'How many legs has a dog?' the best answer is 'four', which is the mode. Some dogs have three legs, so the mean number of legs is probably about 3.99, but this is not a useful answer.

The **median** is the middle number when the numbers are arranged in order. It is a **robust** measure of location that is insensitive to extreme values. The median of the sample of tree heights above is 3, and it would still be 3 if the number 8 were changed to 28, or to any large unknown number.

Although we can calculate the value of the sample mean, what we really want to know is the value of the population mean (symbol μ, pronounced 'mu'). The sample mean is merely an **estimator**. In general, sample statistics estimate population **parameters**.

Measures of Dispersion

We have been considering the heights of trees in a forest and we have estimated that the population mean is 4 metres, based on a random sample of five trees. Does this mean that all the trees are exactly 4 metres tall? Of course not! Some are taller and some are shorter. If we built a wall 4 metres tall, in front of the forest, some of the trees would extend above the top of wall, and others would stop short of it. There is a difference (or **error**, or **deviation**) between the height of each tree and the height of the wall. The average difference (i.e. the typical error, the **standard deviation**) is a useful summary measure of **dispersion** or **spread** or **variability**. The sample standard deviation is the root-mean-square deviation and it is calculated as follows.

Data: 2, 8, 5, 2, 3
Deviations: −2, +4, +1, −2, −1
Squared: 4, 16, 1, 4, 1
Mean: (4 + 16 + 1 + 4 + 1) / 4 = 6.5
Root: $\sqrt{6.5} = 2.5495$

This is the sample standard deviation and it is denoted by the letter **s**. It estimates the population standard deviation, which is denoted by σ, pronounced sigma.

Formula 1.4

Sample Standard Deviation (Raw Data)

$$s = \sqrt{\frac{\Sigma (X-\bar{X})^2}{n-1}}$$

Formula 1.5

Sample Standard Deviation (Frequency Data)

$$s = \sqrt{\frac{\Sigma f(X-\bar{X})^2}{\Sigma f-1}}$$

Note that the standard deviation is the typical error, not the maximum error. Also, the word 'error' does not refer to a mistake: it just means that the trees are not all the same height.

Did you notice that when calculating the mean of the squared deviations, we divided by 4 rather than 5? This quantity, **n−1**, is called the **degrees of freedom**. It can be defined as the number of independent comparisons available. Five trees provide four comparisons: one tree would tell us nothing at all about variability. Dividing by **n−1** in this way ensures that **s** is an unbiased estimator of σ.

The standard deviation squared is called the **variance**. The symbol for the population variance is σ^2, and s^2 denotes its sample estimate. The variance is useful in calculations, but the standard deviation is easier to interpret and talk about.

The sample mean and standard deviation can be easily found using a calculator in statistical mode. Follow these steps.

1. Choose statistical mode.
2. Type the first number and then press the data entry key. (In the case of frequency data, type the number, then press the frequency key, then type the frequency, and finally press the data entry key.)
3. Repeat the above step for every number.
4. Press the relevant key to see the mean.
5. Press the relevant key to see the standard deviation.
6. When you are finished, choose computation mode.

Some processes are expected to achieve a target result. For production and service processes, the target is the nominal value; for measurement processes, the target is the correct value. A process is said to be **accurate** (or **unbiased**) if the process mean is on target. A process is said to be **precise** if the standard deviation is small, i.e. the results are close together.

Cumulative Frequency

Sometimes it is useful to construct a table of cumulative frequencies. **Cumulative frequency** (**F**) means the frequency of occurrence of values less than or equal to the current **X** value. A cumulative frequency table for the journey-time data is shown below.

Table 1.3

Journey Time (X)	Cumulative Frequency (F)
39	0
44	30
49	50
54	67
59	74
64	80
69	84
74	91
79	95
84	97
89	98
94	98
99	100

A graph of cumulative frequency is called a **sigmoid** or an **ogive**.

The median can be read off an ogive by drawing a horizontal line at the 'middle' frequency and reading the corresponding **X** value. In this example, the median = 49. The 25th and 75th **percentiles** (also called the first and third **quartiles**) can be read in the same way (Q1 = 44, Q3 = 61). The **interquartile range** (Q3−Q1) is a measure of dispersion (61 − 44 = 17). If this is divided by two it is called the **semi-interquartile range** or the **quartile deviation** (17/2 = 8.5).

Fig 1.16

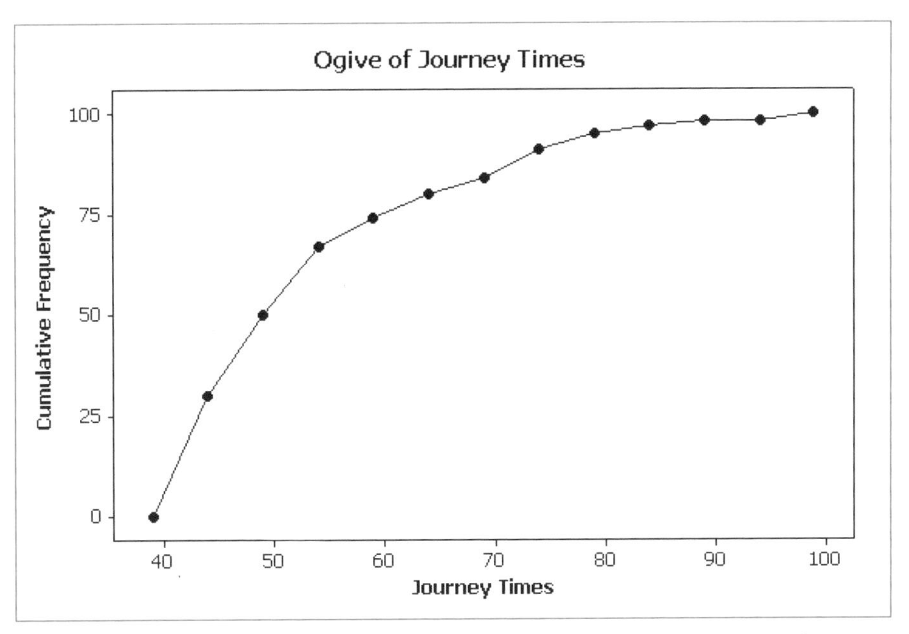

The **range** is another measure of dispersion. The range is the difference between the largest and smallest values in a data set. Unfortunately the sample range is a biased estimator of the population range. It is also sample size dependent, and sensitive to outliers.

> **Having completed this chapter you should be able to:**
> - draw a sample from a population;
> - organise data into a frequency table;
> - construct a histogram;
> - put into words the information revealed in a graph;
> - use a calculator in statistical mode.

Problems 1.3

1. Estimate the mean and the standard deviation of each of these populations, based on the sample data provided.
   (a) Points awarded to a gymnast: 7, 8, 9.
   (b) Shoe-sizes of tram passengers: 8, 11, 2, 9, 6, 12.

(c) Ages of sports-club members: (Use the mid-interval values, i.e. 12.495 etc.)

Table 1.4

Age	Frequency
10–14.99	2
15–19.99	8
20–24.99	16
25–29.99	22
30–34.99	40
35–49.99	8

(d) The Forecourt Transactions data. See Problems 1.1
(e) The Tablet Weights data. See Problems 1.1.
(f) First guess the mean and standard deviation of the number of letters per word in this sentence, and then use your calculator to see how you did.

2. Three vertical lines are drawn on a frequency curve, one each at the mean, the median and the mode. Identify which of (a), (b) and (c) below corresponds to each measure of location.
   (a) This line divides the area under the frequency curve in half.
   (b) This line touches the tallest point on the frequency curve.
   (c) This line passes through the centre of gravity of the area under the frequency curve.

3. (Project) Select a sample of 100 measurements from any population of your choice, and write a report in the following format.
   (a) Define the population of interest and the measurement of interest.
   (b) Carefully describe how the sample was selected from the population.
   (c) Show the raw data.
   (d) Present a frequency table.
   (e) Construct a histogram.
   (f) Comment on what the shape of the histogram tells you about the population.
   (g) Present the sample mean. Comment on what it tells you about the population.
   (h) Present the sample standard deviation. Comment on what it tells you about the population.
   (i) Define another similar population. How would you expect it to differ from your population with respect to the mean, the standard deviation, and the shape of the distribution?

2 UNCERTAINTY

At the end of this chapter you will be able to:

- define probability from two different standpoints;
- calculate the probabilities of simple and compound events;
- calculate the reliability of a system of components.

Virtually all processes involve uncertainty. This is obvious in the case of simple games of chance played with cards and dice, and more complex games such as horse-racing and team sports. But uncertainty is also present in business processes, manufacturing processes and scientific measurement processes. We cannot be certain about the future behaviour of a customer, or the exact status of a unit of product.

Probability

Although we cannot be absolutely certain, we can have a high degree of confidence that a particular event will occur. This confidence is based on the **probability** of the event. Probability is a measurement of how often the event occurs, or how likely it is to occur.

For example, when a coin is tossed, the probability of 'heads' is one-half. This means that if the coin is tossed many times, it is expected that heads will occur about half of the time. Tossing a coin is an example of a **random experiment**, i.e. an experiment whose outcome is uncertain. A single toss is called a **trial**. Heads is an example of an **outcome**. An **event** is a particular outcome, or set of outcomes, in which we are interested.

Probability: Definition 1 – 'how often'

The probability of an event means how often the event occurs. It is the proportion of occurrences when many trials are performed.

$p = 1$ implies that the event always occurs.
$p = 0$ implies that the event never occurs.
In general, $0 \le p \le 1$.

Probability: Definition 2 – 'How likely'

The probability of an event is a measure of how likely the event is to occur on a single future trial.

This definition is meaningful even when only one trial is performed, e.g. a single toss. The value of a probability is not changed by this definition, e.g. the probability of heads is still 50%. The only difference is that we are looking at probability from a different standpoint. We are about to toss a coin once, and we wish to express how likely it is that heads will occur.

Now, $p = 1$ implies that the event is certain to occur.
And $p = 0$ implies that the event is certain not to occur.

Calculating Probability

We have already claimed that the probability of heads, when a coin is tossed, is a half. We use a capital letter to denote an event, so we may write:

$P(H) = 1/2$

Why is the probability of heads calculated by dividing one by two? Because there are two sides on the coin (two possible outcomes) and only one of these is heads. This approach is valid only because the different outcomes (heads and tails) are equally likely to occur. It would not be true to say that the probability that it will snow in Dublin tomorrow is one-half, because the two outcomes ('snow' and 'no snow') are not equally likely.

Formula 2.1

> **Classical Probability**
> If all the outcomes of a trial are equally likely, then the probability of an event is
> $P(E)$ = The number of ways the event can occur ÷ The number of possible outcomes.

Note that this formula, like most formulae related to probability, has a condition associated with it. The formula must not be used unless the condition is satisfied.

We now consider how to calculate the probabilities of events which do not lend themselves to the classical approach. For example, what is the probability that when a thumb-tack is tossed in the air, it lands on its back, pointing upwards? Recall our first definition of probability: the probability of an event means the proportion of occurrences of the event, when many trials are performed. We can perform a large number of trials, and count the number of times it lands on its back. If it lands on its back r times, out of n trials, then $p = r/n$ estimates the probability of the event. Of course, the result will be only an estimate of the true probability: to get a perfect answer, we would have to repeat the trial an infinite number of times.

Formula 2.2

> **Empirical Probability**
> When a large number of trials are performed, the probability of an event can be estimated by the formula
> P(E) = The number of times the event occurred ÷ The total number of trials performed.

There are some events whose probabilities cannot be calculated, or estimated, by either of the two formulae presented above: for example, the probability that a particular horse will win a race, or the probability that a particular company will be bankrupt within a year. These events do not satisfy the conditions associated with either classical probability or empirical probability. To estimate the probabilities of such events, we simply make a guess. The more we know about horse-racing, or business, the more reliable our guess will be. This approach is called subjective probability. In such cases it is common to refer to the **odds** of an event rather than its probability.

Formula 2.3

> **Odds**
> $$Odds = \frac{p}{1-p}$$

For example, if the probability of your team's winning this weekend is 0.8, then the odds are 4 to 1. Bookmakers quote the odds that an event will not occur, and would offer a price of 4 to 1 on the opposition.

Permutations and Combinations

The formula for classical probability, presented earlier, states that if all the outcomes of a trial are equally likely, then the probability of an event is

> P(E) = (The number of ways the event can occur) ÷ (The number of possible outcomes).

In the coin-tossing example considered earlier, the numerator and the denominator of this fraction were simple to compute. But there are cases where it is not simple – for example, when calculating the probability that a player matches 4 of the 6 winning numbers in a lottery. In cases like this, where things are being arranged or selected, formulae are required for **factorials**, **permutations** and **combinations**.

Formula 2.4

Factorial

The number of ways of arranging **n** things in order is '**n** factorial', written **n!**

$$n! = n.(n-1).(n-2)...3.2.1$$

Example: In how many different ways can the letters A, B and C be arranged?
Answer: 3! = 3.2.1 = 6
In this situation, three different letters can be chosen to be put first. After the first letter has been chosen, there is a choice of two letters for second position. That leaves one letter which must go in third place. The arrangements are ABC, ACB, BAC, BCA, CAB, and CBA.

Formula 2.5

Permutations

The number of ways of arranging **r** things, taken from among **n** things, is '**n** permutation **r**', written $^{n}P_{r}$

$$^{n}P_{r} = \frac{n!}{(n-r)!}$$

Example: The 'result' of a horse race consists of the names, in order, of the first three horses past the finishing post. How many different results are possible in a seven-horse race?
Answer: $^{7}P_{3}$ = 7.6.5.4.3.2.1 / (4.3.2.1) = 7.6.5 = 210
In this situation, seven different horses can finish in first place. After the first place has been awarded, there are six possibilities for second position. After the first and second places have been awarded, there are five possibilities for third place.

Formula 2.6

Combinations

The number of sets of **r** things that can be taken from among **n** things is '**n** combination **r**', written $^{n}C_{r}$. The order in which the things are taken does not matter.

$$^{n}C_{r} = \frac{n!}{r!(n-r)!}$$

Example: In how many different ways can 6 numbers be chosen from among 42 numbers in a lottery game?
Answer: $^{42}C_{6}$ = 42!/6!/36! = 42.41.40.39.38.37/(6.5.4.3.2.1) = 5245786
If the six numbers had to be arranged in the correct order, then the answer would be $^{42}P_{6}$. But because the order does not matter, we divide this by 6!, which is the number of arrangements possible for the 6 numbers.

PROBLEMS 2.1

1. Give two explanations of each of the statements below:
   (a) The probability of a 'six' on a roll of a die is one-sixth.
   (b) The probability that an invoice will be paid within 30 days is 90%.
   (c) The probability that a pig flies is 0.

2. Calculate, or estimate, the probabilities of each of the following events:
   (a) A number greater than four occurs when a die is rolled.
   (b) When a thumb-tack is tossed in the air, it lands on its back, pointing upwards.
   (c) The current Taoiseach will be Taoiseach on the first of January next year.

3. In consultation with some others, try to agree on fair odds for an upcoming sporting event. Compare your estimate with a bookmaker's odds.

4. In how many different orders can 8 different numbers be arranged?

5. Leah, Josiah and John are three members of a class of 20 students. A raffle is held among the members of the class. Each member has one ticket, and the three winning tickets are drawn from a hat.
   (a) What is the probability that Leah wins first prize, Josiah wins second prize, and John wins third prize?
   (b) What is the probability that Leah, Josiah and John are the three prize-winners?

6. It has already been calculated that there are 5245786 ways in which 6 numbers can be chosen from among 42 numbers in a lottery game. In how many different ways can 36 numbers be chosen from among 42 numbers? Explain.

7. Explain in words why $^{n}P_{n} = n!$

8. Explain in words why $^{n}C_{n} = 1$.

The Laws of Probability

Thus far we have considered single events. We now consider how probability is calculated for combinations of events. We can use the words 'not', 'and' and 'or' to describe virtually any combination of events.

The 'NOT' Rule

If an event, such as a 'six' on a die, occurs one-sixth of the time, then the complement of this event, '**not** six', occurs the rest of the time, i.e. five-sixths of the time. This principle is true for any event, so the formula which follows has no special condition associated with it.

Formula 2.7

> **The 'NOT' Rule**
> For any event A:
> P(not A) = 1 − P(A)

Example: S denotes a 'Six'
P(S) = 1/6
P(not S) = 1 − 1/6 = 5/6

The Simple Multiplication Rule

The simple **multiplication rule** deals with simple cases involving '**and**'. Consider a game in which a player rolls a die and tosses a coin. The player wins only if the die shows a 'six' and the coin shows 'heads'. Each time the game is played, we could look at the die first of all: if the die shows a 'six', then we can proceed to look at the coin. If the die does not show a 'six', then there is no need to look at the coin. If we proceed in this way, then we will look at the coin on one-sixth of all plays, and on one-half of these occasions we will see 'heads', making a win. So the proportion of plays that result in a win ('six' and 'heads') is one-half of one-sixth. 'Of' means multiply.

We are assuming that the probability of 'heads' on the coin is one-half, even after we have got a 'six' on the die. The coin is not any more likely to show 'heads' after the die has shown a 'six', neither is it less likely to do so. We say that the two events are **independent**. This means that the occurrence of one event does not change the probability of occurrence of the other event.

Formula 2.8

> **The Simple Multiplication Rule**
> For independent events, A, B:
> P(A and B) = P(A) × P(B)

Example: S denotes a 'Six', P(S) = 1/6
H denotes 'heads', P(H) = 1/2
P(S and H) = 1/6 × 1/2 = 1/12
This rule can be extended to deal with more than two events.

The Simple Addition Rule

The simple **addition rule** deals with simple cases involving '**or**'. Suppose that a die is rolled and we are interested in the event 'a six or an odd number'.
S denotes a 'six', P(S) = 1/6
U denotes 'an odd number', P(U) = 3/6

Note that these two events, S and U, cannot occur at once. We say that S and U are

mutually exclusive, i.e. if S occurs then U cannot occur, if U occurs then S cannot occur. To put it another way, **P**(S and U) = 0.

To calculate the probability of 'S or U', we add the individual probabilities.

P(S or U) = **P**(S) + **P**(U) = 1/6 + 3/6 = 4/6

This answer is reasonable, since there are four outcomes which satisfy the event 'S or U': namely 1, 3, 5 and 6.

Formula 2.9

> **The Simple Addition Rule**
> For mutually exclusive events, A, B:
> **P**(A or B) = **P**(A) + **P**(B)

Example: S denotes a 'six', **P**(S) = 1/6
U denotes 'an odd number', **P**(U) = 3/6
P(S or U) = **P**(S) + **P**(U) = 1/6 + 3/6 = 4/6
This rule can be extended to deal with more than two events.

The General Multiplication Rule

This rule deals with all cases involving 'and'. Consider the following experiment. A letter is drawn at random from among the 26 letters of the alphabet. L denotes the event 'the letter drawn is from the second half of the alphabet (N to Z)'. V denotes the event 'the letter drawn is a vowel'.

P(L) = 13/26 = 1/2

P(V) = 5/26, but if L has occurred, then it is not 5/26, but rather 2/13, because there are only two vowels in the second half of the alphabet.

We call this the **conditional probability** of V given L, and write it as **P**(V|L).

Because **P**(V) ≠ **P**(V|L), the events L and V are not independent.

To compute **P**(L and V), we multiply **P**(L) by **P**(V|L).

P(L and V) = 1/2 . 2/13 = 2/26 = 1/13 which is obviously correct, since there are two letters which are vowels, and are in the latter half of the alphabet (O and U).

Formula 2.10

> **The General Multiplication Rule**
> For any events, A, B:
> **P**(A and B) = **P**(A) × **P**(B|A)

Example: L denotes 'a letter is from the second half of the alphabet'
P(L) = 1/2
V denotes 'a vowel'
P(V) = 5/26, **P**(V|L) = 2/13
P(L and V) = **P**(L) × **P**(V|L) = 1/2 × 2/13 = 2/26 = 1/13

The General Addition Rule

This rule deals with all cases involving 'or'. A die is rolled. Consider the following events:
U denotes 'an odd number', **P**(U) = 3/6
F denotes 'a number less than five', **P**(F) = 4/6
What is **P**(U or F)?

Obviously, the answer is not 3/6 + 4/6 = 7/6, since this is greater than 1. These two events are not mutually exclusive. Both events can occur at once, namely when a 'one' or a 'three' occurs; hence **P**(U and F) = 2/6. When we added 3/6 + 4/6, these two outcomes were counted twice. To compensate for this, we must subtract **P**(U and F) to give the answer as 5/6.

Formula 2.11

The General Addition Rule
For any events, A, B:

P(A or B) = **P**(A) + **P**(B) − **P**(A and B)

Example: U denotes 'an odd number', **P**(U) = 3/6
F denotes 'a number less than five', **P**(F) = 4/6
P(U or F)= **P**(U) + **P**(F) − **P**(U and F)
= 3/6 + 4/6 − 2/6
= 5/6

De Morgan's Rule

De Morgan's rule provides a simple way to replace an expression involving 'or' with an equivalent expression involving 'and', and vice versa. This can be convenient, for example, if the word 'or' arises with independent events.

Formula 2.12

De Morgan's Rule
To replace an expression with an alternative, equivalent expression, follow these three steps:

1. Write 'not' before the entire expression.
2. Write 'not' before each event in the expression.
3. Replace every 'and' with 'or', and every 'or' with 'and'.

Example: A or B ≡ not (not A and not B)

Example: A game involves tossing a coin and rolling a die, and the player 'wins' if either 'heads' or a 'six' is obtained. Calculate the probability of a win.
H denotes 'heads', **P**(H) = 1/2

S denotes a 'Six', **P**(S) = 1/6
P(win) = **P**(H or S)
H and S are not mutually exclusive events.
But H and S are independent events, so let us write:
P(win) = **P**(not (not H and not S))
P(H) = 1/2, **P**(not H) = 1/2
P(S) = 1/6, **P**(not S) = 5/6
P(win) = 1 −(1/2 × 5/6)
P(win) = 1 – 5/12
P(win) = 7/12

Solving Problems

When you are presented with a problem in probability, the first step is to identify the separate events involved. Next, re-phrase the problem, using only the words 'and', 'or' and 'not' to connect the events. Next, consider how multiplication, addition, etc., can be used to calculate the probability of this combination of events, paying particular attention to the relevant assumptions in each case. Also, look out for short-cuts, e.g. if the event is complex, it may be simpler to calculate the probability that it does not occur, and subtract the result from one.

Example: A husband and wife take out a life insurance policy for a twenty-year term. It is estimated that the probability that each of them will be alive in twenty years is 0.8 for the husband and 0.9 for the wife. Calculate the probability that, in twenty years, just one of them will be alive.

Solution:
Identify the separate events:
H: The husband will be alive in twenty years. **P**(H) = 0.8
W: The wife will be alive in twenty years. **P**(W) = 0.9
Rephrase the problem; 'just one of them' means:
H and not W or not H and W
'or' becomes '+' because the mutually exclusive property holds; 'and' becomes 'multiply' assuming independence.
Required is
P(H) × **P**(not W) + **P**(not H) × **P**(W)
= 0.8 × 0.1 + 0.2 × 0.9
= 0.08 + 0.18
= 0.26

PROBLEMS 2.2

1. A single letter is drawn at random from the alphabet. The following events are defined:
   W: the letter W is obtained.
   V: a vowel is obtained.
   Calculate the probability of each of the following events:
   (a) W
   (b) V
   (c) W or V.
2. A coin is tossed and a die is rolled. The following events are defined:
   H: the coin shows 'heads'.
   S: the die shows a 'six'.
   Compute the probabilities of the following events:
   (a) H
   (b) S
   (c) H and S
   (d) H or S.
3. A die is rolled twice. Compute the probability of obtaining:
   (a) two sixes
   (b) no sixes
   (c) a six on the first roll but not on the second roll
   (d) at least one six
   (e) exactly one six.
4. Three coins are tossed simultaneously. Calculate the probability of obtaining:
   (a) three heads
   (b) at least one head.
5. A firm submits tenders for two different contracts. The tenders will be assessed independently. The probability that the first tender will be successful is 70%, and the probability that the second tender will be successful is 40%.
   Calculate the probability that:
   (a) both will be successful
   (b) neither will be successful
   (c) only the first will be successful
   (d) only the second will be successful
   (e) at least one will be successful.
6. In a lottery game a player selects 6 numbers, from a pool of 42 numbers. Later, the winning numbers are announced. These consist of a set of 6 randomly selected numbers from the pool. Another 'bonus' number is also randomly selected. Calculate the probability that, on a single play, a player achieves:

(a) the grand prize, i.e. all six winning numbers
(b) a 'match five', i.e. just any five of the winning numbers
(c) a 'match four', i.e. just any four of the winning numbers
(d) a 'match three and the bonus number', i.e. just any three of the winning numbers and also the bonus number.

Reliability

Reliability is defined as the probability that a product will function as required for a specified period. Where a product consists of a system of components whose individual reliabilities are known, the reliability of the system can be calculated.

Components in Series

When components are in **series** it means that all the components must function in order for the system to function. Most systems are like this.

Example: A torch consists of a battery, a switch and a bulb, assembled in series. The reliabilities of the battery, switch and bulb are 0.9, 0.8 and 0.7 respectively. Calculate the system reliability.

Fig 2.1

Components in Series

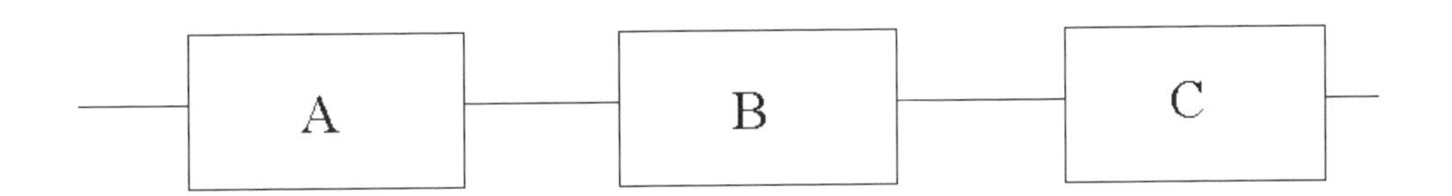

A: battery functions, **P**(A) = 0.9
B: switch functions, **P**(B) = 0.8
C: bulb functions, **P**(C) = 0.7
P(torch functions) = **P**(A and B and C)
Assuming independence
P(torch functions) = **P**(A) × **P**(B) × **P**(C)
P(torch functions) = 0.9 × 0.8 × 0.7= 0.504
The independence condition requires that a good battery has the same chance of being combined with a good switch, as does a bad battery, etc. This condition tends to be satisfied by random assembly.

Formula 2.13

> **Reliability of a System of Components in Series**
> The reliability of a system of components in series, assuming independence, is the product of the reliabilities of the individual components.

Components in Parallel

Parallel systems include components in back-up mode. If one component fails, there is another component to take its place. The back-up components can be either in standby mode, such as a standby generator to provide power during a mains failure, or in active mode, such as stop-lamps on a vehicle, where all of the components are active even before one fails.

Example: The reliability of the mains power supply is 0.99 and the reliability of a standby generator is 0.95.
Calculate the system reliability.

Fig 2.2

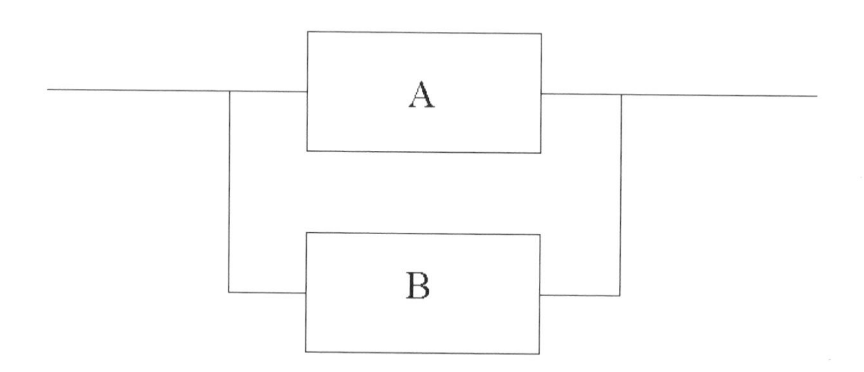

A: mains functions, **P**(A) = 0.99, **P**(not A) = 0.01
B: generator functions, **P**(B) = 0.95, **P**(not B) = 0.05
P(system functions) = **P**(A or B)
P(system functions) = 1 − **P**(not A and not B)
Assuming independence
P(system functions) = 1 – 0.01 × 0.05
P(system functions) = 1 – 0.0005 = 0.9995

Formula 2.14

> **Reliability of a System of Components in Parallel**
> The unreliability of a system of components in parallel, assuming independence, is the product of the unreliabilities of the individual components. (Unreliability = 1 – reliability).

Complex Systems

Complex systems contain subsystems. The reliability of each subsystem should be calculated first. The subsystem can then be regarded as a single component.

Example: A projector has two identical bulbs and one fuse. The reliability of a bulb is 0.9 and the reliability of a fuse is 0.95. All other components are assumed to be 100% reliable. Only one bulb is required for successful operation. Calculate the reliability of the projector.

Fig 2.3

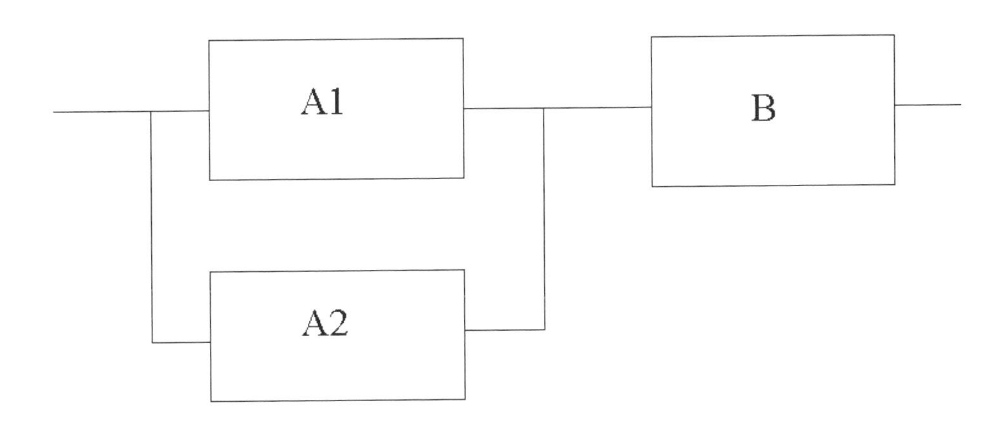

A1: bulb 1 functions, **P**(A1) = 0.9, **P**(not A1) = 0.1
A2: bulb 2 functions, **P**(A2) = 0.9, **P**(not A2) = 0.1
A: bulb subsystem functions
P(A) = 1 – 0.1 × 0.1
P(A) = 1 – 0.01 = 0.99
P(projector functions) = **P**(A and B)
P(projector functions) = 0.99 × 0.95 = 0.9405

Reliability has traditionally been applied to tangible products consisting of assembled components; but it can also be applied to service systems consisting of stages such as diagnosis, prescription and compliance. Business transactions can be treated as systems in which the components include ordering, delivery and billing.

Having completed this chapter you should be able to:

- appreciate the dual meaning of probability;
- calculate the probabilities of simple events;
- use the laws of probability to solve problems involving probability and reliability.

PROBLEMS 2.3

1. An electric convector heater consists of an element, a switch, and a fan assembled together. These three components are independent and will operate successfully for a year with probabilities 0.92, 0.98 and 0.97, respectively.
   (a) Calculate the probability that the heater will operate successfully for a year.
   (b) If two such heaters are purchased, calculate the probability that both heaters will operate successfully for a year.
   (c) If two such heaters are purchased, calculate the probability that neither of them will operate successfully for a year.
   (d) If two such heaters are purchased, calculate the probability that at least one of them will operate successfully for a year.
   (e) If the heater is redesigned to include a second element (similar to the first element and as a back-up for it), what is the probability that the redesigned heater will operate successfully for a year?

2. A vacuum cleaner (Model M1) consists of a power supply, a switch and a motor assembled in series. The reliabilities of these components are 0.95, 0.90 and 0.80, respectively.
   (a) Calculate the reliability of a Model M1 vacuum cleaner. Also, if a customer buys two Model M1 vacuum cleaners, in order to have a second vacuum cleaner available as a back-up, calculate the reliability of the system.
   (b) If a customer buys two Model M1 vacuum cleaners, in order to have a second vacuum cleaner available to provide spare parts as required, calculate the reliability of the system.
   (c) A model M2 vacuum cleaner is made from the same components as Model M1, but it has a second motor included as a back-up. Therefore a model M2 vacuum cleaner consists of a power supply, a switch, a motor and a back-

up motor, each with reliabilities as described above. Calculate the reliability of a Model M2 vacuum cleaner.

(d) If a customer buys two Model M2 vacuum cleaners, in order to have a second vacuum cleaner available to provide spare parts as required, calculate the reliability of the system.

3. It is estimated that 30% of blues fans, who are aware of an upcoming concert, will order tickets. A TV advertising campaign will reach an estimated 65% of fans. A billboard campaign will reach an estimated 45% of fans.
What proportion of blues fans will order tickets?

3

MODELS

At the end of this chapter you will be able to:

- recognise some common statistical distributions;
- calculate probabilities associated with these distributions.

An experiment such as rolling a die is called a **random experiment**, because the outcome is uncertain. And because the outcome is a number, that number is called a **random variable**. All we can say for sure is that the number will be from the **sample space** {1, 2, 3, 4, 5, 6}, and that all these outcomes are equally likely. The **probability distribution** is shown below, and the probabilities add up to 1 because some number must occur.

Fig 3.1

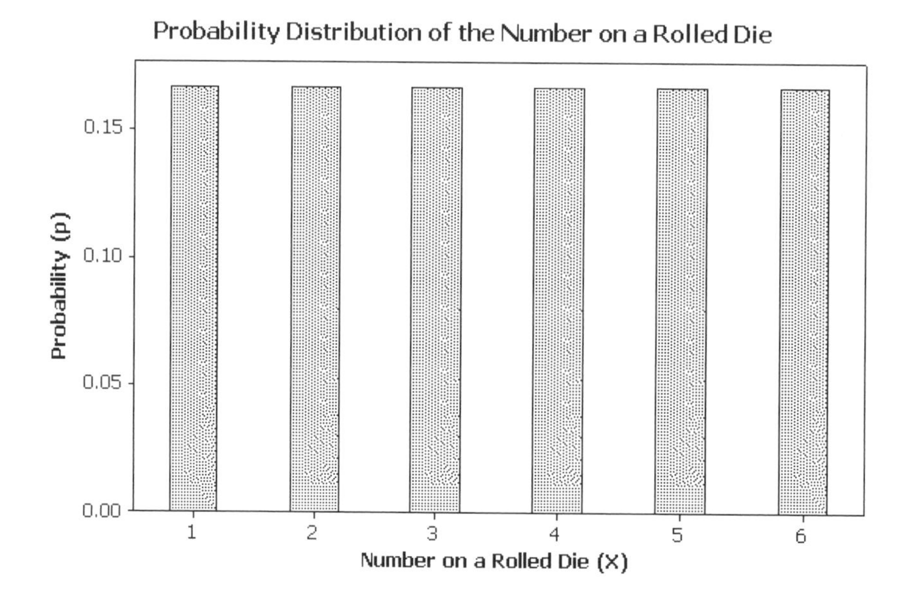

Selecting a random digit gives rise to a similar situation. The same rule applies about the outcomes being equally likely. The probability distributions even look alike, having bars that are equally tall.

Fig 3.2

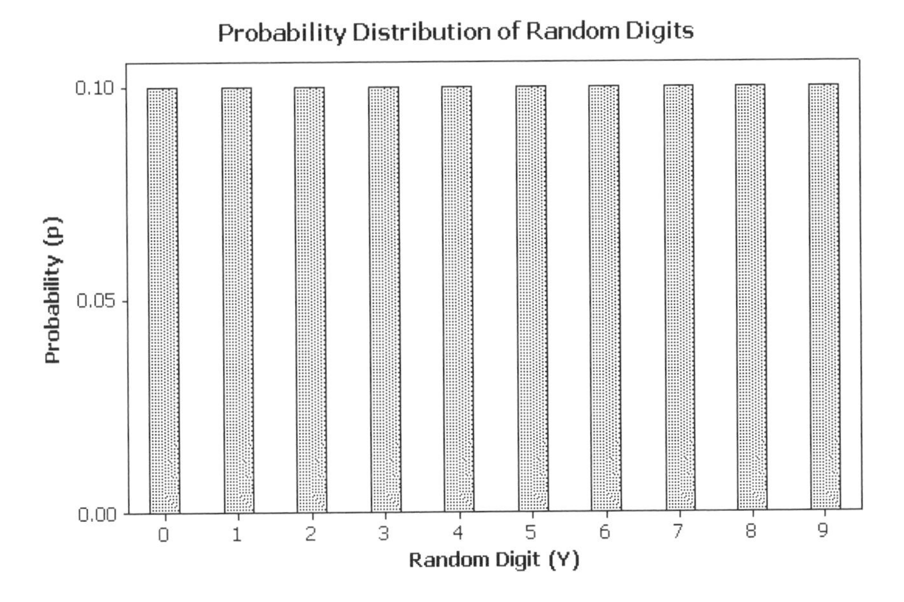

These random variables are alike in that they are from the same family, called the **uniform distribution**. They are different members of the family as can be seen from their different **parameter** values, **k** = 6 and **k** = 10, where a parameter means a number that is constant within a given situation.

In general, if we can name the distribution that a random variable belongs to, then we have a model that describes its behaviour. This can be useful in two ways. Firstly, if the data fit the model well, we can estimate the parameters and the probability of occurrence of any value of the variable. Secondly, if the data are not a good fit to the model, this suggests that the independence and randomness assumptions are not true, thus providing unexpected insight into the process.

The Normal Distribution

The **normal distribution** describes a wide variety of variables, including measurements that occur in nature, manufacturing dimensions, and errors of measurement. It always has the same characteristic bell shape. The normal distribution has two parameters: the mean, μ, and the standard deviation, σ.

The normal distribution is a continuous distribution, not a discrete distribution. The total area under the curve is 1. The height of the curve is called the **probability density**.

The probability of occurrence of a value in any particular range is the area under the curve in that range.

Fig 3.3

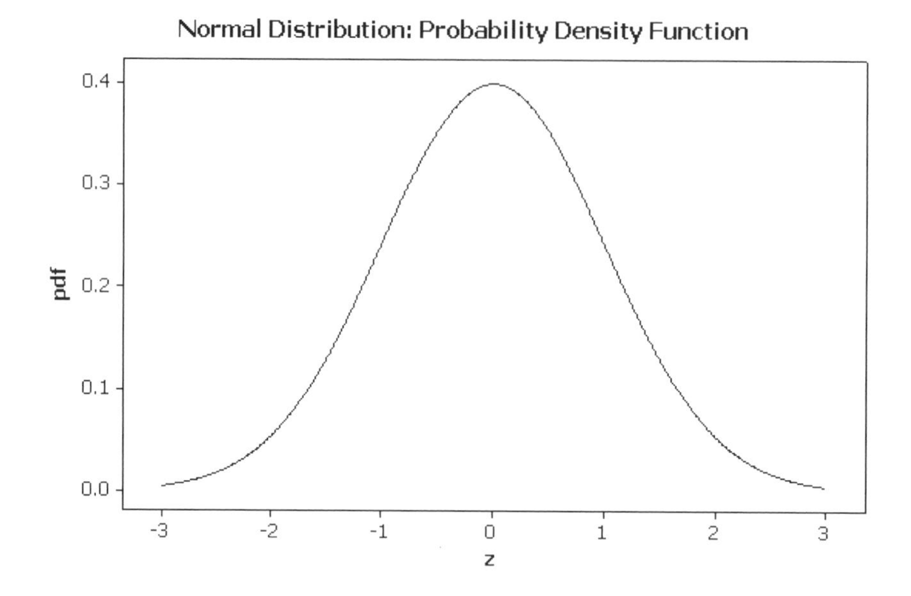

To calculate normal probabilities, we first compute the 'standard normal score', **z**.

Formula 3.1

Normal Distribution

$$z = \frac{X - \mu}{\sigma}$$

z is the 'standard normal score'.

The **z**-score means, 'How many standard deviations above the mean is this value?' It follows that **z** = 0 represents the mean, while positive **z**-scores represent values above the mean, and negative **z**-scores represent values below the mean. The normal distribution table gives the cumulative probability corresponding to any positive **z**-score.

Example 1: The heights of men are normally distributed with mean, $\mu = 175$ cm, and standard deviation, $\sigma = 10$ cm. What proportion of men are taller than 182.5 cm?

Solution: $z = (X - \mu) / \sigma$

$z = (182.5 - 175) / 10$

$z = 0.75$

Fig 3.4

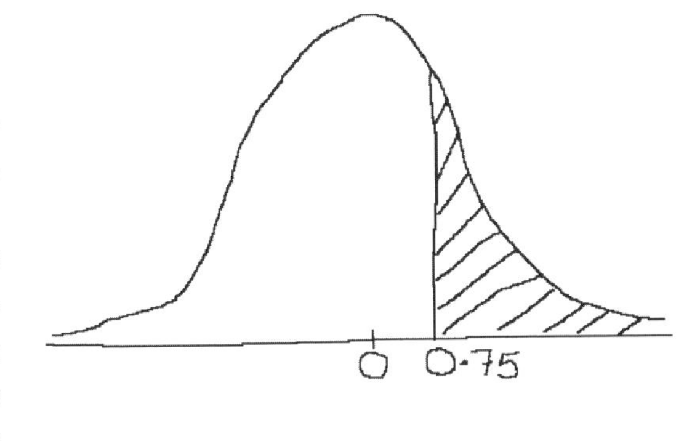

At this point, we sketch a bell-curve with zero in the middle. We mark our **z**-score on the left or right as appropriate (on the right this time, because we have +0.75), and shade the area to the left or right of **z** as appropriate (to the right this time, because we have 'taller than'). We now ask ourselves whether the shaded area is a minority or a majority of the total area under the curve (a minority this time, i.e. we expect that the answer < 0.5).
The normal table gives 0.7734, a majority.
We require $1 - 0.7734 = 0.2266$.
22.66% of men are taller than 182.5 cm.

Example 2: The heights of men are normally distributed with mean, $\mu = 175$ cm, and standard deviation, $\sigma = 10$ cm. What proportion of men are between 165 cm and 170 cm in height?
Solution: These two **X** values will correspond to two **z**-scores.
$X_1 = 165$, $X_2 = 170$
$z_1 = -1$, $z_2 = -0.5$

Fig 3.5

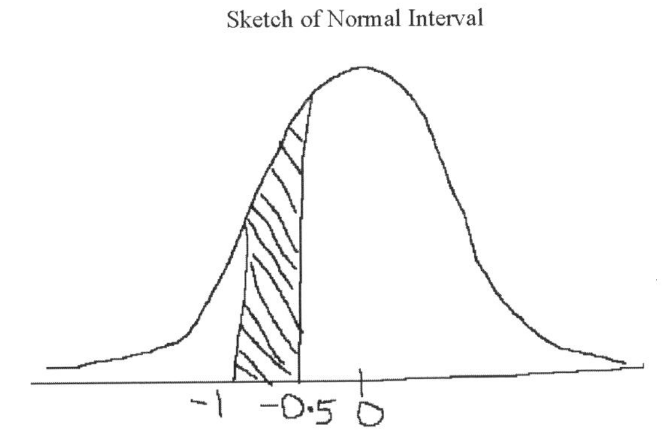

The following four steps can be used to find the probability corresponding to an interval.
Left tail area $= 1 - 0.8413 = 0.1587$
Right tail area $= 0.6915$
Total tail area $= 0.8502$
Interval area $= 1 - 0.8502 = 0.1498$.
14.98% of men are between 165 cm and 170 cm in height.

PROBLEMS 3.1

1. What proportion of a normal distribution has a **z**-score that is:
   (a) greater than zero?
   (b) less than 1?
   (c) greater than 1?
   (d) between -1 and 1?
   (e) between -1.5 and 2.17?
   (f) between 1.2 and 2.7?
   (g) between -1.76 and -1.36?
   (h) between -3 and 3?
   (i) between -1.96 and 1.96?

2. The heights of corn stalks are normally distributed with mean $\mu = 16$ cm, and standard deviation $\sigma = 2$ cm. Calculate the proportion of these stalks that are:
   (a) shorter than 14 cm
   (b) between 13 cm and 17 cm
   (c) shorter than 17.5 cm
   (d) taller than 18.25 cm
   (e) taller than 13.8 cm
   (f) between 13.2 cm and 18 cm
   (g) between 17.6 cm and 18.4 cm
   (h) taller than 16 cm
   (i) taller than 30 cm
   (j) between 11 cm and 13.5 cm.

3. A manufacturing process makes penicillin tablets each with a nominal weight of 250 mg. The process mean is 250.2 mg, and the standard deviation is 0.6 mg. The specification limits are: upper specification limit = 252 mg, lower specification limit = 248 mg. What proportion of the tablets conforms to specification?

4. The heights of women are normally distributed with mean 167.5 cm and standard deviation 7.5 cm. A range of T-shirts are made to fit women of different heights as follows:
   Small T-shirt: 155 to 165 cm
   Medium T-shirt: 165 to 175 cm
   Large T-shirt: 175 to 185 cm.
   What percentage of the population is in each category, and what percentage is not catered for?

The Binomial Distribution

The **binomial distribution** describes the number of occurrences of an event, on a fixed number of similar trials. On each trial the event may either occur or not occur.

The binomial distribution has two parameters:

n, the number of trials, and

p, the probability of occurrence on a single trial.

Examples of binomial variables include: the number of bull's-eyes achieved when a player throws three darts; the number of orders received by a telesales company in response to 5000 calls; the number of 'yes' answers given to a question posed to 1000 respondents in an opinion poll; the number of defective handsets in a sample of twenty handsets.

The trials are assumed to be independent, i.e. if the first dart hits the bull's-eye, this does not affect the second throw. The probability of occurrence is the same on each trial, and does not change due to confidence, tiredness, etc.

The formula below can be used to calculate binomial probabilities by hand.

Formula 3.2

Binomial Distribution

$$P(r) = {}^{n}C_{r} \times p^{r} \times (1-p)^{n-r}$$

n = the number of trials

p = the probability of occurrence on a single trial

r = the exact number of occurrences

P(r) is the probability of exactly **r** occurrences.

Example: 10% of eggs are brown. If 6 eggs are packed, at random, into a carton, what is the probability that exactly two are brown?

$n = 6$

$p = 0.1$

$r = 2$

$P(r) = {}^{n}C_{r} \times p^{r} \times (1-p)^{n-r}$

$P(2) = {}^{6}C_{2} \times (0.1)^{2} \times (1 - 0.1)^{6-2}$

$P(2) = {}^{6}C_{2} \times (0.1)^{2} \times (0.9)^{4}$

$P(2) = 15 \times 0.01 \times 0.6561$

$P(2) = 0.098415$

The probability that a carton contains exactly two brown eggs is 0.098415, or, to put it another way, 9.84% of all such cartons contain exactly two brown eggs.

The complete probability distribution is shown below.

Fig 3.6

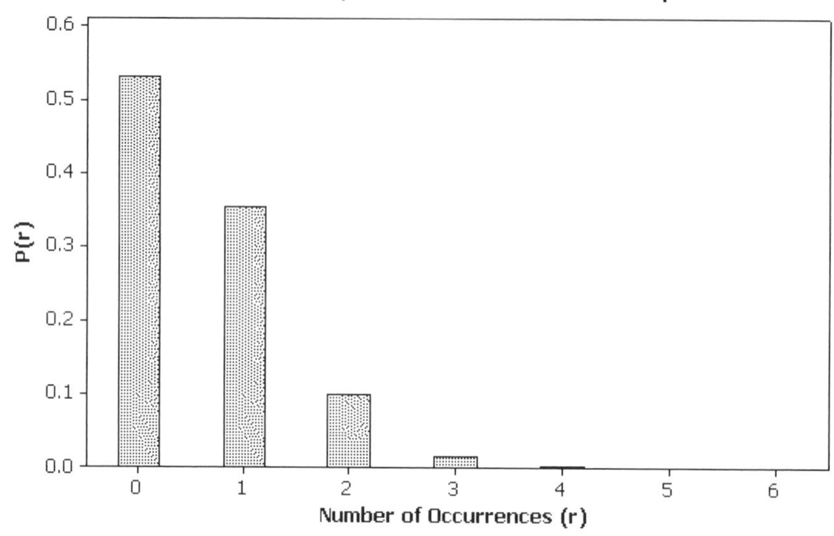

Sometimes we are not interested in an exact number of occurrences, but in any number of occurrences more than, or less than, some threshold value.

Example: A jury consists of 12 citizens, selected at random, from a population which is 55% female. What is the probability that the jury will have at least two female members?

n = 12

p = 0.55

'at least two' means that **r** = 2 or 3 or ... or 12.

P('at least two') = **P**(2) + **P**(3) + ... + **P**(12)

(the probabilities can always be added because the exact outcomes are mutually exclusive)

P('at least two') = 1 – [**P**(0) + **P**(1)]

(if the list of values consists of more than half the total number, use the **r** values not on the list instead, and subtract their sum from 1)

P(0) = $^{12}C_0 \times 0.55^0 \times (0.45)^{12}$ = 0.000069

P(1) = $^{12}C_1 \times 0.55^1 \times (0.45)^{11}$ = 0.001011

P(0) + **P**(1) = 0.001080

1 – 0.001080 = 0.998920.

99.89% of juries will have at least two female members.

The complete probability distribution is shown below.

Fig 3.7

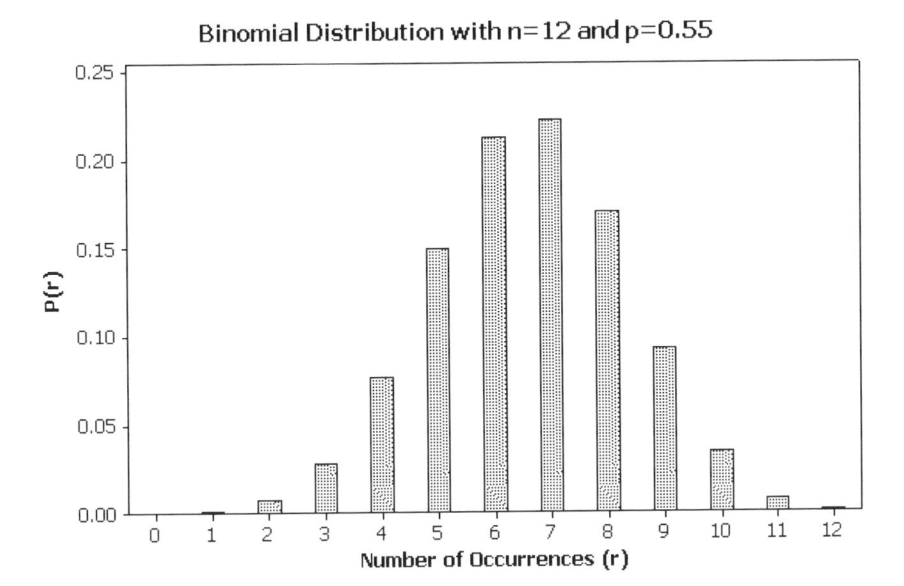

Here is an alternative solution to the jury problem:

Formula 3.3

> **Normal Approximation to the Binomial Distribution**
>
> $\mu = n.p$ and $\sigma = \sqrt{n.p(1-p)}$
>
> are the parameters of the normal approximation to the binomial distribution, subject to the conditions $n.p \geq 5$ and $n.(1-p) \geq 5$.

$\mu = 12 \times 0.55 = 6.6$
$\sigma = \sqrt{(12 \times 0.55 \times 0.45)} = 1.723$
'at least two' means that $\mathbf{X} \geq 1.5$
(Note the correction for continuity. Because the normal distribution is continuous and the binomial distribution is discrete, all the values between 1.5 and 2.5 are allocated to $\mathbf{r} = 2$.)
$\mathbf{z} = (1.5 - 6.6) / 1.723 = -2.96$
The normal table gives 0.9985.
99.85% of juries will have at least two female members.
This answer approximates closely to the exact answer obtained using the binomial distribution.

Problems 3.2

1. Which of the following variables are binomially distributed?

   Q: the number of left-handed people sitting at a table of four people

   R: the number of red cars in a random sample of 20 cars

   S: the time taken by a show-jumping contestant to complete the course

   T: the outdoor temperature on a summer's day

   U: the number of months in a year in which there are more male than female births in a maternity unit

   V: the number of weeds in a flower-bed

   W: the weight of a banana

   Y: the duration of a telephone call

   Z: the number of players on a football team who receive an injury during a game.

2. Construct the complete probability distribution for the number of heads obtained when a coin is tossed four times, i.e. calculate **P**(0), **P**(1), **P**(2), **P**(3), and **P**(4). Verify that the sum of these probabilities is 1, and explain in words why this is so.

3. Seeds are sold in packs of 10. If 98% of seeds germinate, calculate the probability that when a pack of seeds are sown:

   (a) more than eight will germinate

   (b) eight or fewer will germinate.

4. A certain machine produces gaskets, 5% of which are defective. Every hour a patrol inspector selects a sample of 6 gaskets at random and inspects them. What proportion of these samples contain:

   (a) exactly two defectives?

   (b) more than two defectives?

   (c) two defectives, at most?

   (d) fewer than two defectives?

   (e) at least two defectives?

5. 10% of customers pay by direct debit. In a random sample of 300 customers, what is the probability that fewer than 40 pay by direct debit?

6. 5% of airline passengers fail to show up for their flights. Out of a random sample of 150 passengers, what is the probability that more than 10 fail to show up?

The Poisson Distribution

The **Poisson distribution** describes the number of occurrences of an event, within a fixed interval of opportunity.

The Poisson distribution has one parameter, λ, the mean number of occurrences per interval.

Examples of Poisson variables include: the number of fish caught in a day; the number of potholes on a 1 km stretch of road; the number of scratches on a window-pane; the number of cherries in a pot of cherry yogurt. These examples show that the interval can be an interval of time, or of length, or of area, or of volume. There is no limit, in theory, to the number of times the event could occur. These events could be called 'accidents', or simply 'random events'. It is assumed that the events are independent, e.g. if a fish has been caught in the past 5 minutes, that does not make it any more, or less, likely that a fish will be caught in the next five minutes. The formula below can be used to calculate Poisson probabilities by hand.

Formula 3.4

Poisson Distribution

$$P(r) = \frac{e^{-\lambda} \times \lambda^r}{r!}$$

λ = the mean number of occurrences per interval

P(**r**) is the probability of exactly **r** occurrences.

Example: A company receives three complaints per day on average. What is the probability of receiving more than one complaint on a particular day?

$\lambda = 3$

'more than one' means that **r** = 2 or 3 or 4 or …

P('more than one') = **P**(2) + **P**(3) + **P**(4) + …

P('more than one') = 1 – {**P**(0) + **P**(1)}

P(0) $= e^{-3} \times 3^0 / 0! = 0.0498$

P(1) $= e^{-3} \times 3^1 / 1! = 0.1494$

P(0) + **P**(1) = 0.1992

1 – 0.1992 = 0.8008.

80% of days will have more than one complaint.

The complete probability distribution is shown below.

Fig 3.8

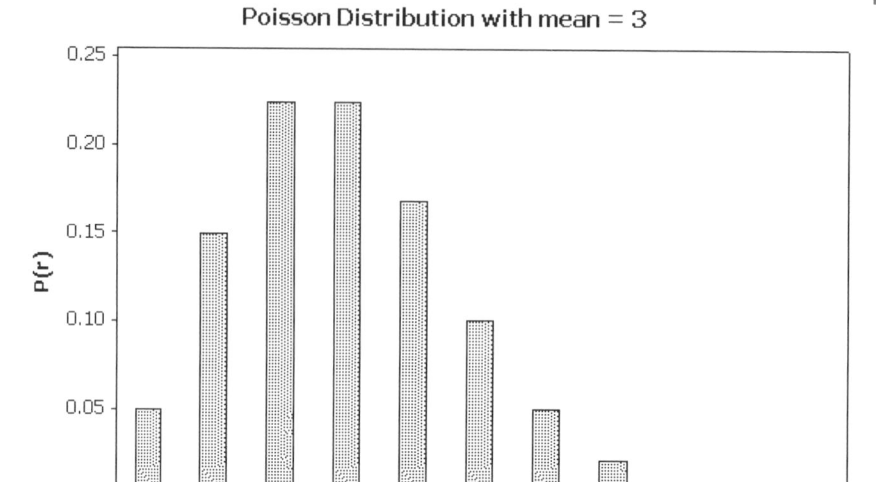

Problems 3.3

1. Which of the following variables are Poisson distributed?

   N: the number of goals scored in a football match

   O: the number of students per year that are kicked by horses in a riding school

   P: the number of days in a week on which the **Irish Independent** and the **Irish Times** carry the same lead story

   Q: the weight of a cocker spaniel puppy

   R: the number of crimes committed in Dublin in a weekend

   S: the number of telephone calls received per hour at an enquiry desk

   T: the number of weeds in a flower-bed

   U: the length of an adult's step

   V: the number of bulls-eye's a player achieves with three darts.

2. The number of customers who enter a shop, per hour, is Poisson distributed with mean 8. Calculate the percentage of hours in which:

   (a) fewer than two customers enter

   (b) more than two customers enter.

3. The number of blemishes that occur on a roll of carpet during manufacture is Poisson distributed, with mean 0.4 blemishes per roll. What percentage of rolls is classified as:

   (a) 'perfect', having no blemishes

   (b) 'seconds', having one or two blemishes

   (c) 'scrap', i.e. all the rest.

Other Distributions

The following is a brief introduction to some common distributions. The **exponential** distribution describes the intervals between random (i.e. Poisson) events. As such, it provides a simple model for product lifetimes, provided that failures occur at random. The **Weibull** distribution is a more flexible lifetime model that can take account of burn-in and wear-out fail modes. The **lognormal** distribution is a positively skewed distribution that is useful for describing populations where the larger values can be very large, such as total bacteria counts.

How can we know what distribution to fit to a set of data? Ideally, we may know that the process operates in a way that satisfies certain assumptions and so we choose the corresponding distribution. If we have no such prior knowledge, we can look at a histogram of the data to see whether its shape reminds us of some distribution. We can follow this up by checking the fit of one or more distributions using a **probability plot**. This procedure is explained here using the normal distribution.

The normal probability density function was illustrated in Fig 3.3. The normal cumulative density function is shown below.

Fig 3.9

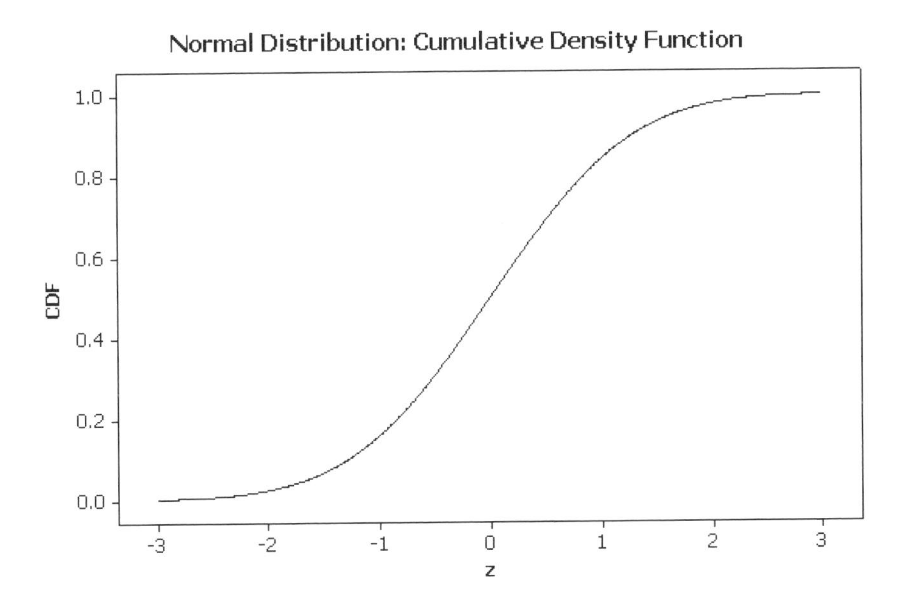

This curve is sigmoidal in shape, but if the two ends of the vertical axis were stretched, it could be made linear. This is what a probability plot does. It plots the cumulative probabilities using a suitably transformed vertical axis, so that if the data are normal, the graph will be linear.

Fig 3.10

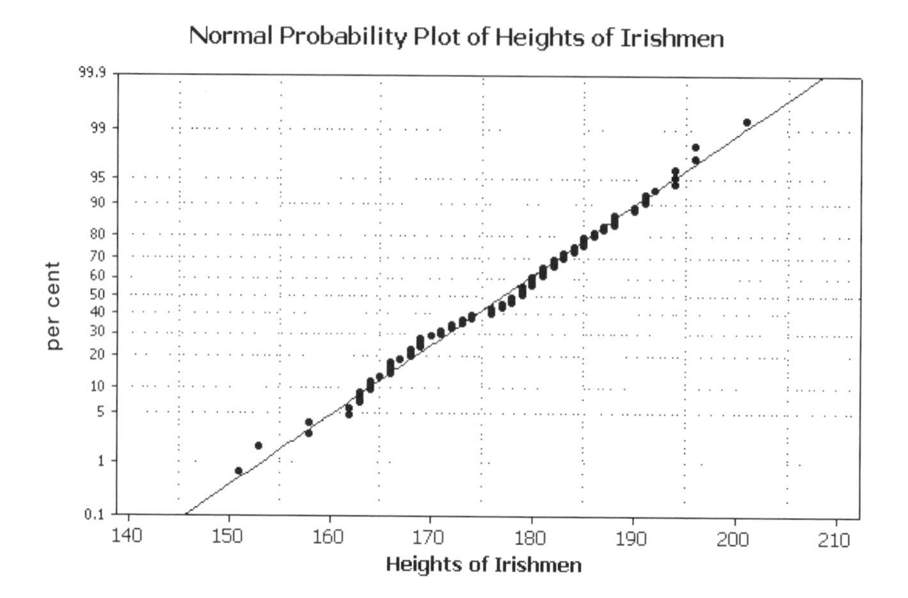

The plot above indicates that the heights of Irishmen are quite normal. There is some scatter, which we expect anyway, but the points are approximately linear.

The graph below is a normal probability plot of the times spent waiting for a taxi. The graph shows clearly that the data are not normal. This would also be obvious from a histogram.

Fig 3.11

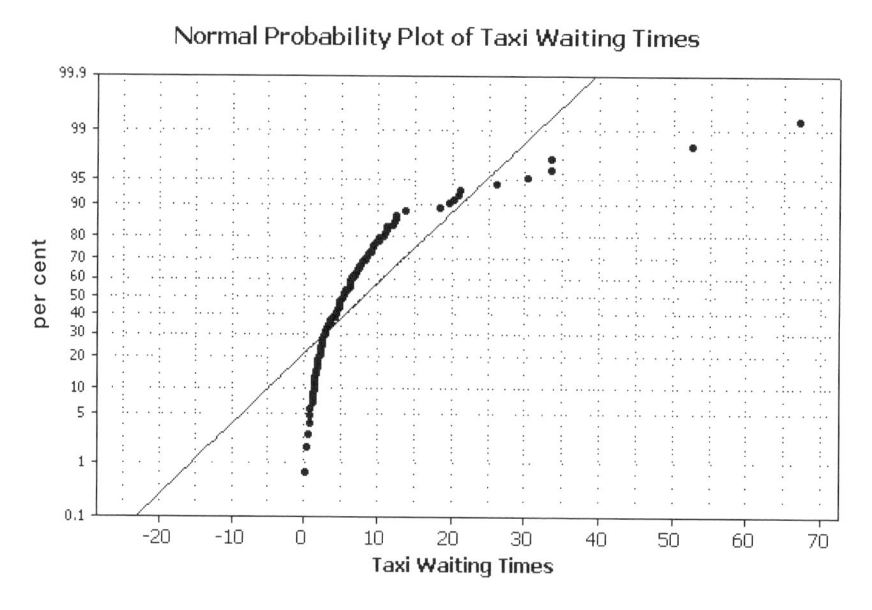

A lognormal distribution is a good fit to the taxi data.

Fig 3.12

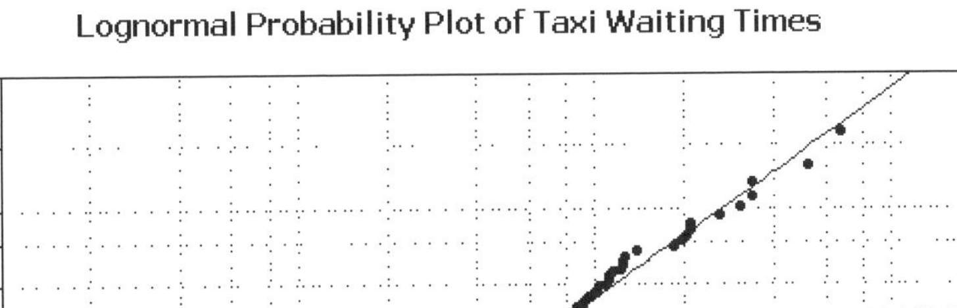

Having completed this chapter you should be able to:

- recognise binomial, Poisson and normal processes;
- use model parameters to calculate probabilities;
- assess the goodness-of-fit of distributions to data using probability plots.

4

ESTIMATION

At the end of this chapter you will be able to:

- construct confidence intervals for means, proportions and standard deviations;
- determine the sample size required to make an estimate;
- compare two populations and estimate the magnitude of the difference between their means or proportions.

We begin this chapter by exploring a number of ideas in relation to variation and sampling. Our discoveries will culminate in a set of formulae that can be used to estimate unknown parameters with a stated degree of confidence.

The Addition of Variances

Example: An Easter-egg set consists of a chocolate egg and a chocolate bar in a presentation box. The eggs weigh 100 g on average, and the bars 50 g, and their standard deviations are 4 g and 3 g respectively. It is easy to see that the sets have a mean net weight of 150 g. But what is the standard deviation of the weights of the sets? When the eggs are already in the boxes, before the bars are added, the standard deviation of the weights of chocolate in the boxes is already 4 g. When the bars are added, the standard deviation must increase, because more variation is being introduced. However, it will not increase to $4 + 3 = 7$, because that would happen only if we always put a heavy bar with a heavy egg ($100 + 4 + 50 + 3$). The standard deviation of the weights of the sets is actually 5, because $4^2 + 3^2 = 5^2$. This result might remind you of Pythagoras's theorem. It shows why the variance is a useful measure of dispersion. Variances can be added together to find the total variance, provided that the sources of variation are independent. This independence condition is satisfied by random assembly, because there is no tendency to combine heavier eggs with heavier, or lighter, bars.

Example: After lawnmowers are manufactured, they are supplied with an initial quantity of petrol for an engine test. The initial quantities supplied are 100 ml on average, and the test uses 50 ml on average, with standard deviations of 4 ml and 3 ml, respectively.

It is easy to see that the average remaining quantity is 50 ml (100 − 50); but what is the standard deviation of the remaining quantity?

As before, when the test quantities are used up the standard deviation must increase, because more variation is being introduced. The result is 5 again. Note that the variances are added together, regardless of whether the means are added or subtracted.

Example: The task of framing a picture can be broken down into a number of activities, namely preparation, cutting and assembly. The average times, in minutes, required to complete these activities are 40, 20 and 10, with standard deviations of 12, 4 and 3, respectively. Find the mean and the standard deviation of the total time for the task.

Mean = 40 + 20 + 10 = 70 minutes

Variance = 144 + 16 + 9 = 169

Standard deviation = 13 minutes

Note that the principle of addition of variances applies to any number of sources of variation.

Formula 4.1

The Addition of Variances

The total variance that arises from any number of independent sources (1, 2, 3, ...) is $\sigma^2_{total} = \sigma^2_1 + \sigma^2_2 + \sigma^2_3 \cdots$

Expected Value and Standard Error

Example: The weights of individual toffee sweets are described as having mean μ and standard deviation σ. These sweets are packed randomly into bags (samples) with **n** sweets per bag. Suppose we buy a bag every day and take the trouble to write down the bag weight and also the sample mean (i.e. bag weight ÷ n).

The bag weights can be described as follows:

Mean = $n\mu$, variance = $n\sigma^2$, standard deviation = $\sqrt{n}\sigma$

The sample means can be described as follows:

Mean = μ, standard deviation = $\sigma/\sqrt{n}$

These last two quantities, the mean and the standard deviation of the sample means, are usually called the **expected value** of the sample mean, and the **standard error** of the sample mean.

Formula 4.2

The Expected Value of the Sample Mean

$E(\overline{X}) = \mu$

This formula is not surprising at all. It confirms that a sample mean is an unbiased estimator of the population mean, provided that the sample is random. We could also say that this formula merely states that the sweets do not get heavier, or lighter, as a result of being packed in bags.

Formula 4.3

The Standard Error of the Sample Mean

$$SE(\overline{X}) = \frac{\sigma}{\sqrt{n}}$$

This is a very useful result. It confirms our intuition that a more precise estimate of μ is provided by a sample, rather than by an individual value, and that larger samples are preferable to smaller samples. In other words, sample means are less variable than individual values. When we combine this information with our next discovery, below, we will be in a position to calculate the exact degree of confidence that can be placed in an estimate of a population mean.

The Central Limit Theorem

This next discovery is very surprising. We already know that statistical populations can have many different shapes. We might expect that the distribution of sample means from these populations would also have different shapes. But this is not so! Sample means all have the same distribution, no matter what population the samples are taken from. For example, the population of numbers on a rolled die has a uniform shape.

Fig 4.1

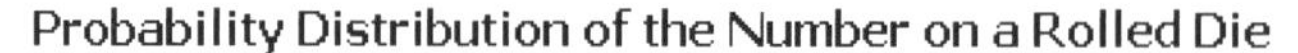

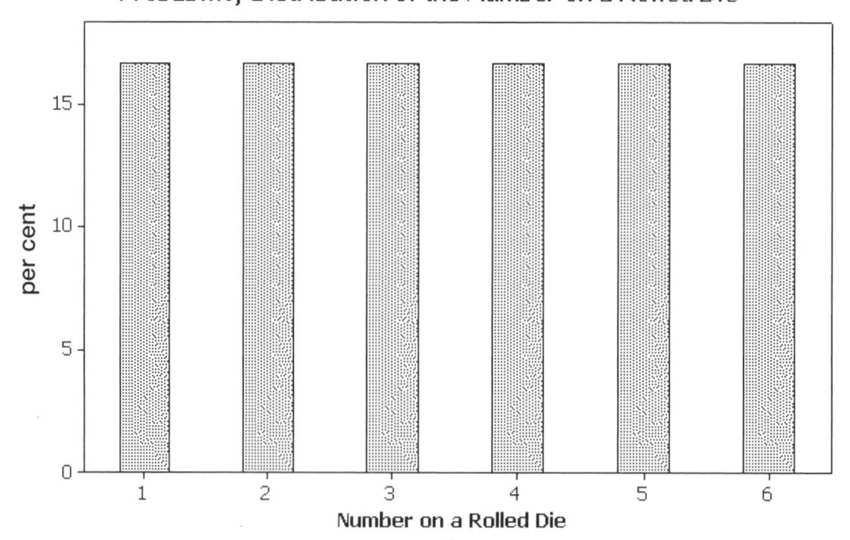

Now consider sample means for n = 2 dice. The sample mean is more likely to be in the middle than at the extremes. To get a sample mean of 1, both dice must show 1, but there are lots of ways to get a sample mean of 3: namely 3 and 3, 1 and 5, 5 and 1, 2 and 4, 4 and 2.

Fig 4.2

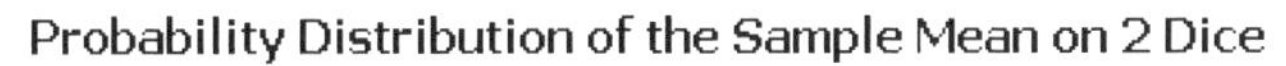

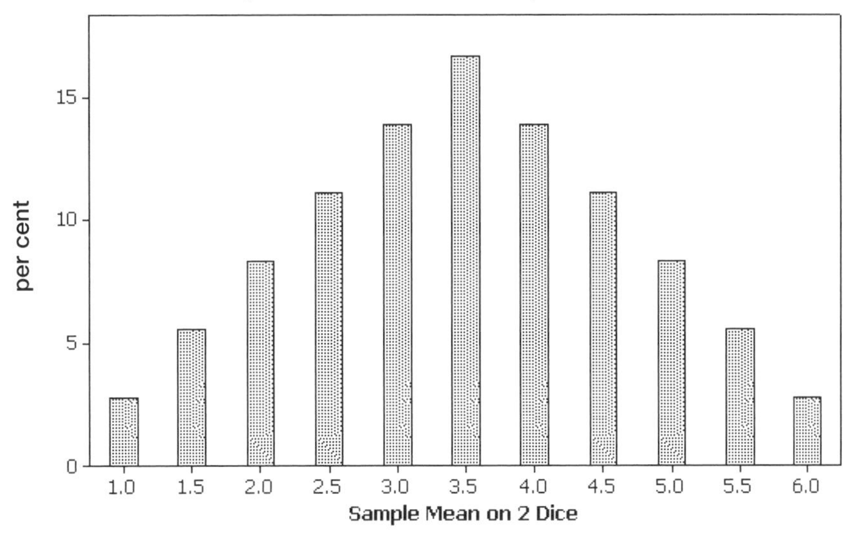

Consider sample means for n = 5 dice.

Fig 4.3

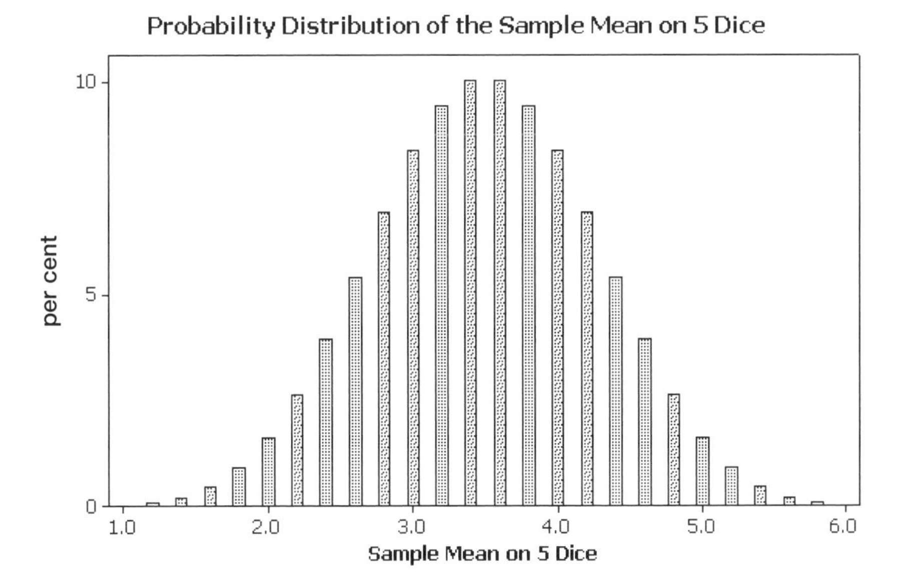

The distribution is normal. Sample means taken from **any** population are normally distributed if the samples are big enough. And how big is 'big enough'? If the parent population is normal, then $n = 1$ is big enough; if it is symmetric, then $n = 5$ is usually big enough; very skewed populations require larger **n**.

Our cumulative discoveries so far can be summarised by a particular formulation of the **Central Limit Theorem**.

Formula 4.4

> **The Central Limit Theorem**
> When random samples of size **n** are drawn from **any** population with mean μ and standard deviation σ, the sample means tend towards a normal distribution, with expected value μ, and standard error $\sigma/\sqrt{n}$.

Confidence Interval for a Mean or Proportion

Confidence Interval for a Mean

We now know the exact distribution of the sample mean. Therefore if we take just one sample from any population, we know that the sample mean comes from a theoretical sampling distribution, which is normally distributed with expected value μ, and standard error $\sigma/\sqrt{n}$. But we also know that there is a probability of 95% that a value from a normal distribution has a **z**-score lying within the interval –1.96 to +1.96. Hence there is a 95% probability that the sample mean lies within 1.96 standard errors of the population mean. So we can use the sample mean to construct a **confidence interval** that contains the unknown population mean with 95% probability.

Formula 4.5

> **95% Confidence Interval for a Population Mean (if σ is known)**
>
> $$\mu = \overline{X} \pm 1.96 \frac{\sigma}{\sqrt{n}}$$

This formula can be used only if σ is known. There are situations where this is the case. Suppose I pick up a stone and weigh it 1000 times on a kitchen scale. The results will differ slightly from each other, because the scale is not perfect. I can calculate the mean of the results, and this tells me something about the stone – how heavy it is. I can also calculate the standard deviation of the results, but this tells me nothing about the stone. It tells me something about the scale – how precise it is. Now if you pick up a different stone and begin to weigh it, we know what standard deviation to expect for your results. It will be the same as mine, because you are using the same weighing process. So whether you decide to weigh your stone once, or five times, we can use the formula above to estimate your process mean, because we already know the standard deviation from previous experience. In summary, if we have prior knowledge of the standard deviation of a process, we can use this knowledge to estimate the current process mean.

Example: The cycle times of a washing machine are known to have a standard deviation of 2 seconds. Construct a 95% confidence interval for the population mean, if a random sample of three cycles had the following durations, in seconds: 2521, 2526, 2522.

$\overline{X} = 2523$

$\sigma = 2$

$n = 3$

$\mu = 2523 \pm 1.96 \times 2 / \sqrt{3}$

$\mu = 2523 \pm 2.26$

$2520.74 \leq \mu \leq 2525.26$

We can state with 95% confidence that the mean of all the cycle times lies inside this interval. On 95% of occasions when we construct such a confidence interval, the interval will include the population mean. There is a 5% probability that an unfortunate sample has been drawn, leaving the population mean lying outside the interval. Other confidence levels, such as 99%, could be used instead, but this book uses 95% throughout. The simple estimate, 2523, is called a **point** estimate.

It would be great if the previous formula could be used with a population having an unknown standard deviation. Perhaps we could replace σ in the formula with its sample estimate, **s**. However, because **s** is only an estimate of σ, we would lose some of our confidence, and we would have less than 95% confidence in the result. One way to restore our confidence would be to widen the interval by using a number bigger than 1.96. But what number should we use? This problem was solved in 1908 by W. S. Gossett, a statistician at Guinness's brewery in Dublin. Writing under the pen-name 'Student', Gossett gave us the **t**-distribution. The **t**-distribution is closely related to the normal distribution, but while the normal **z**-score measures in units of σ, the **t**-score measures in units of **s**. The **z**-score can be defined as 'the number of standard deviations that a value is above the mean', but the **t**-score is defined as 'the number of estimated standard deviations that a value is above the mean'. There is actually a different **t**-distribution for every different number of degrees of freedom, **n − 1**, on which the standard deviation estimate is based. We now have a confidence-interval formula that requires no prior knowledge of the population; all we need is a random sample. Formula 4.5 is a special case of Formula 4.6, because $t_{\infty} = z$. This formula represents the culmination of all the preceding theory in this chapter.

Formula 4.6

95% Confidence Interval for a Population Mean (if σ is unknown)

$$\mu = \overline{X} \pm t_{n-1} \frac{s}{\sqrt{n}}$$

Example: Random sample flight times, in minutes, between Dublin and Edinburgh were as follows: 45, 49, 43, 51, 48. Construct a 95% confidence interval for the population mean.

$\overline{X} = 47.2$

$s = 3.19$

$n = 5$

$t_{n-1} = 2.776$

$\mu = 47.2 \pm 2.776 \times 3.19 / \sqrt{5}$

$\mu = 47.2 \pm 3.96$

$43.24 \leq \mu \leq 51.16$

We can state with 95% confidence that the mean flight time, for all flights between Dublin and Edinburgh, lies between 43.24 and 51.16 minutes.

Confidence Interval for a Proportion

A population proportion means the proportion of units in a population that possess some attribute of interest, such as satisfied customers, or defective products. A sample proportion, $P = r/n$, is an unbiased estimate of the population proportion, π, with standard error $\sqrt{\{\pi(1-\pi)/n\}}$. If π is unknown, then the standard error is also unknown, but it can be estimated by $\sqrt{\{P(1-P)/n\}}$. Hence the following formula provides an approximate confidence interval for π. An exact confidence interval, based on the binomial distribution, can be obtained by an iterative procedure, but it is too tedious for calculation by hand.

Formula 4.7

Approximate 95% Confidence Interval for a Population Proportion

$$\pi = P \pm 1.96 \sqrt{\frac{P(1-P)}{n}}$$

Example: Of 50 students randomly selected from a college, 16 had been bitten by a dog at some time. Construct an approximate 95% confidence interval for the population proportion.

$P = 16 / 50 = 0.32$

$\pi = 0.32 \pm 1.96 \sqrt{\{0.32 \times (1 - 0.32) / 50\}}$

$\pi = 0.32 \pm 0.13$

$0.19 \leq \pi \leq 0.45$

We estimate that between 19% and 45% of all students in the college had been bitten by a dog at some time, with approximately 95% confidence.

Problems 4.1

1. A process that fills bags with rice is known to have a standard deviation of 0.5 grams. Construct a 95% confidence interval for the population mean, if a random sample of filled bags had net weights as follows:
   7.15, 8.21, 7.93, 7.46, 8.91, 7.61
2. It is known that the standard deviation of a thickness-measuring device is 0.05 mm. Five repeat measurements were made, with the following results:
   12.01, 12.05, 12.08, 12.02, 12.11
   Construct a 95% confidence interval for the population mean.
3. A random sample of service calls involved journeys of the following distances, in km:
   17.1, 9.2, 4.0, 3.1, 20.7, 16.1, 11.0, 14.9
   Construct a 95% confidence interval for the population mean.
4. A motorist randomly selected five insurers and obtained motor-insurance quotations. The quoted cost of cover, in euro per day, was as follows:
   3.01, 2.95, 3.02, 3.05, 2.79
   Construct a 95% confidence interval for the population mean.
5. A random sample of 200 booklets was selected, and 60 of these were found to have defective binding. Construct an approximate 95% confidence interval for the population proportion.
6. Of 633 students surveyed, 105 walk to college. Construct an approximate 95% confidence interval for the population proportion.

Sample Size for Estimation

Larger samples provide more precise estimates. To determine the **sample size** required in any situation, we first need to identify some practical size, $\pm\delta$ (delta), for the width of the interval required. Secondly, we require an estimate of the standard deviation. If no such estimate is available, we simply proceed with a **pilot sample** of any convenient size. The standard deviation of the pilot sample is used to calculate the full sample size required, and then more data can be collected as necessary. The value for the sample size suggested by the formula should be rounded up to the next integer.

Formula 4.8

Sample Size for Estimating a Population Mean

$$n = \left(\frac{1.96 \times \sigma}{\delta}\right)^2$$

Example: A random sample of four fish was taken at a fish-farm. The weights of the fish, in grams, were:
317, 340, 363, 332.

How many fish must be weighed in order to estimate the population mean to within ± 10 grams, with 95% confidence?
s = 19.2 is the sample standard deviation estimate
δ = 10
n = $(1.96 \times 19.2 / 10)^2$
n = 14.16, rounded up becomes 15.
We require 15 fish, i.e. 11 more fish.

To determine the sample size required to estimate a population proportion, we require an initial estimate of the population proportion itself. This can be based on a pilot sample or on our prior knowledge of similar populations. Alternatively, we can use **P** = 0.5, which is the most conservative initial estimate, and will lead to a sample size that is certainly big enough. Sample sizes required for estimating proportions are typically much larger than those required for estimating means. This is because each observation provides only a 'yes' or 'no' response.

Formula 4.9

Sample Size for Estimating a Population Proportion

$$n = \frac{1.96^2 \times P(1-P)}{\delta^2}$$

Example: How large a sample is required to estimate, to within 1%, the level of support among the electorate for a new proposal to amend the constitution?
P = 0.5, conservative initial estimate
δ = 0.01, delta is 1%
n = $1.96^2 \times 0.5 \times (1-0.5) / 0.01^2$
n = 9604
We require a sample of 9604 voters.

PROBLEMS 4.2

1. The lifetimes of three rechargeable batteries were measured, with the following results, in hours:
   168, 172, 163.
   How large a sample is required to estimate the population mean to within ± 1 hour?
2. The standard deviation of the lengths of roof-tiles is known to be 3 mm. How large a sample is required to estimate the population mean to within ±0.5 mm, with 95% confidence?
3. How large a sample is required to estimate, to within 10%, the proportion of pizza orders that require home delivery?
4. How large a sample is required to estimate, to within 3%, the level of support for a political party which traditionally receives 22% support in opinion polls?

Estimating a Standard Deviation

Estimating σ Using a Single Sample

The sample standard deviation estimate, **s**, is based on **n − 1** degrees of freedom. It is an unbiased estimator of the population standard deviation, σ. The divisor is **n − 1** rather than **n**, to compensate for the fact that the estimated deviations are 'too small' as a result of being measured from the sample mean rather than the population mean.

Estimating σ Using Two or More Samples

If samples are available from two or more populations, that are known or assumed to have equal variance, the information in the samples can be combined to provide a **pooled variance estimate**. (In practice, the equal variance assumption is often made to simplify hand calculations.) If the samples are of equal size, the pooled variance estimate is simply the mean of the sample variances. If the samples are of unequal size, a **weighted mean** must be calculated, giving weight to each sample variance in proportion to the number of degrees of freedom on which it is based. The formula for two samples is provided below, and this can easily be extended to deal with more than two samples.

Formula 4.10

Pooled Variance Estimate

$$s^2 = \frac{(n_1-1)s_1^2 + (n_2-1)s_2^2}{n_1-1+n_2-1}$$

Degrees of freedom = $n_1 - 1 + n_2 - 1$

Example: A depth sounder was used to take three repeat measurements at a fixed point near the coast, and another six measurements at a fixed point further out to sea.

The results, in metres, were as follows: 28, 29, 26 (coast) and 36, 38, 37, 35, 35, 36 (sea). Estimate the standard deviation of repeat measurements for this device.

$n_1 = 3$
$s_1 = 1.528$
$n_2 = 6$
$s_2 = 1.169$
$s^2 = \{(3-1) \times 1.528^2 + (6-1) \times 1.169^2\} \div (3-1+6-1)$
$s^2 = 1.643$ is the pooled variance estimate, and
$s = 1.282$ is the pooled standard deviation estimate.

Confidence Interval for σ

When random samples are drawn repeatedly from a normal population, the distribution of the sample standard deviations is related to a **chi-square distribution**. This is a skewed distribution that is bounded below by zero. The exact shape of a chi-square distribution depends on its degrees of freedom, **n − 1**. We can use the upper and lower 2.5% points of the distribution to construct a 95% confidence interval for σ.

Formula 4.11

Confidence Interval for σ

$$\sqrt{\frac{(n-1)s^2}{\chi^2_{upper}}} \le \sigma \le \sqrt{\frac{(n-1)s^2}{\chi^2_{lower}}}$$

Applies to a normally distributed population.

Example: A random sample of five loaves had the following lengths, in cm: 26.9, 28.4, 31.6, 27.8, 30.2.

Construct a 95% confidence interval for sigma, the population standard deviation.

$n = 5$
$s = 1.898$
degrees of freedom, df = 4
From the chi-square table, we find
upper 2.5% point = 11.143
lower 2.5% point = 0.484 (the upper 97.5% point)
$\sqrt{\{4(1.898)^2/11.143\}} = 1.137$
$\sqrt{\{4(1.898)^2/0.484\}} = 5.456$
$1.137 \le \sigma \le 5.456$
Notice that the interval is not symmetric about the point estimate.

Difference between Means or Proportions

Comparing Means Using Paired Data

Often we are interested in the difference between two population means, rather than the means themselves; for example, how much more expensive one retail outlet is compared to another. If possible, it is best to use **paired data**. This means that we purchase the same items in the two retail outlets. This gives rise to pairs of values, one from each population. The advantage of pairing is that we are comparing like with like, and so neither population is favoured by the list of items that are sampled. We calculate the difference between each pair of values, and then use Formula 4.6 to estimate the mean difference.

Example: The prices of a number of randomly selected greengrocery items were compared in two outlets, Mark's and Daniel's. The data below show the price in Mark's followed by the price in Daniel's, in cent.

Table 4.1

Item	Mark	Daniel
Pears	119	135
Lettuce	109	125
Bananas	123	115
Mango	89	123
Avocado	75	105
Lemon	32	48
Celery	99	115

The differences (Mark minus Daniel) are:

−16, −16, +8, −34, −30, −16, −16

$\bar{X} = -17.14$

$s = 13.46$

$n = 7$

$t_{n-1} = 2.447$

$\mu = -17.14 \pm 2.447 \times 13.46 / \sqrt{7}$

$\mu = -17.14 \pm 12.45$

$-29.59 \leq \mu \leq -4.69$

We are 95% confident that Mark's is between 4.69 and 29.59 cent less expensive than Daniel's, per item, on average.

Comparing Means Using Independent Samples

We may wish to compare the cost of rented accommodation in two different areas. In situations like this it is not possible to use paired data, and instead we draw two **independent random samples**, one from each population. Assuming that the population variances are equal, we first compute the pooled variance estimate using formula 4.10, and then use the formula below to construct the confidence interval.

Formula 4.12

Confidence Interval for Difference Between Means

$$\mu_1 - \mu_2 = \bar{X}_1 - \bar{X}_2 \pm t\sqrt{\frac{s^2}{n_1} + \frac{s^2}{n_2}}$$

s^2 is the pooled variance estimate, assuming equal variances.

Example: Two independent random samples were selected, of apartments in Lucan and Naas. The apartments were of a similar size and standard. The monthly rentals, in euro, are shown below. Construct a 95% confidence interval for the population mean difference in monthly rental.

Lucan: 950, 875, 850, 900.

Naas: 825, 850, 875, 880, 860.

First use formula 4.10 to find s^2

$n_1 = 4$

$s_1 = 42.70$

$n_2 = 5$

$s_2 = 21.97$

$s^2 = \{(4-1) \times 42.70^2 + (5-1) \times 21.97^2\} \div (4-1 + 5-1)$

$s^2 = 1057.23$

Now use formula 4.12 to construct the confidence interval.

$X_1 = 893.75$

$X_2 = 858.00$

$df = 7$

$t = 2.365$ from table

$\mu_1 - \mu_2 = 893.75 - 858.00 \pm 2.365 \sqrt{(1057.23/4 + 1057.23/5)}$

$\mu_1 - \mu_2 = 35.75 \pm 51.58$

$-15.83 \leq \mu_1 - \mu_2 \leq 87.33$

We are 95% confident that Lucan is between €15.83 less expensive and €87.33 more expensive than Naas, on average. Because the confidence interval includes zero, it may be the case that the mean difference is zero.

Difference between Proportions

When we estimate a difference between proportions in this context, we are referring to proportions in two distinct populations. For example, we might estimate the difference between the proportion of Wicklow voters who support the Labour Party and the proportion of Mayo voters who support the Labour Party. We would not use this formula to estimate the difference between the proportion of Wicklow voters who support the Labour Party and the proportion of Wicklow voters who support the Green Party.

Formula 4.13

Approximate 95% Confidence Interval for Difference Between Proportions

$$\pi_1 - \pi_2 = P_1 - P_2 \pm 1.96\sqrt{\frac{P_1(1-P_1)}{n_1} + \frac{P_2(1-P_2)}{n_2}}$$

Example: In a sample of 200 shoppers in Liffey Valley Retail Park, 98 purchased clothing. In a sample of 300 shoppers in Blanchardstown Retail Park only 34 purchased clothing. Construct a 95% confidence interval for the difference between the population proportions.

$n_1 = 200$
$P_1 = 98 / 200 = 0.49$
$n_2 = 300$
$P_2 = 34 / 300 = 0.1133$
$\pi_1 - \pi_2 = (0.49 - 0.1133) \pm 1.96 \sqrt{\{0.49 \times (1-0.49)/200 + 0.1133(1-0.1133)/300\}}$
$= 0.3767 \pm 0.0780$
$0.2987 \leq \pi_1 - \pi_2 \leq 0.4547$

We are 95% confident that between 29.87% and 45.47% more shoppers purchased clothing in Liffey Valley Retail Park, compared to Blanchardstown Retail Park.

Having completed this chapter you should be able to:

- construct point and interval estimates of means, proportions and standard deviations;
- identify the sample size required to provide an interval estimate of specified width;
- estimate the magnitude of the difference between means or proportions.

PROBLEMS 4.3

1. Liam weighed himself three times in succession on a scale and the readings, in kg, were: 25.4, 25.6, 24.9. Sean weighed himself twice on the same scale and his results were: 31.2, 31.9. Use all the data to estimate the standard deviation of repeat measurements for this scale.

2. A 100 m hurdler was timed on five practice events, with the following results, in seconds: 12.01, 12.05, 11.99, 12.06, 12.03. Construct a 95% confidence interval for σ.

3. Six internal wall-to-wall measurements were taken with a tape measure, and the same measurements were also taken with a handheld laser device. The results, in cm, are shown below, in the same order each time. Construct a 95% confidence interval for the mean difference.
   Tape Measure: 602, 406, 478, 379, 415, 477.
   Laser Device: 619, 418, 483, 386, 413, 489.

4. Construct a 95% confidence interval for the difference in weight between Liam and Sean in question 1 above.

5. An industrial process fills cartridges with ink. At 10 a.m. a sample of fills were measured, with the following results, in ml: 55, 49, 57, 48, 52. At 11 a.m. another sample was taken: 53, 59, 50, 49, 52. Construct a 95% confidence interval for the difference between the population means.

6. Of a sample of 150 patrons at a theme park in summer, 15 had prepaid tickets. Of a sample of 800 patrons at the theme park in winter, only 9 had prepaid tickets. Construct a 95% confidence interval for the difference between the population proportions.

7. (Project) Collect a sample of 50 attribute observations from any large population, and write a report in the following format.
   (a) Define the population of interest, and the attribute of interest.
   (b) Carefully describe how the sample was selected from the population.
   (c) Construct an approximate 95% confidence interval for the population proportion.
   (d) Calculate the sample size required to estimate the population proportion to within $\pm 1\%$, with 95% confidence.
   (e) Discuss two biases that could have arisen if your sample had not been drawn appropriately.

8. (Project) Select a sample of 10 measurements from any large population of your choice, and write a report in the following format.

(a) Define the population of interest, and the measurement of interest.
(b) Carefully describe how the sample was selected from the population.
(c) Present the data, compute the sample mean and the sample standard deviation, and construct a 95% confidence interval for the population mean.
(d) Explain carefully what your confidence interval tells you.
(e) Discuss two biases that could have arisen if your sample had not been drawn appropriately.

5

TESTING

At the end of this chapter you will be able to:

- formulate a statistical **hypothesis test**;
- use sample data to test hypotheses and state conclusions.

Hypothesis Testing

Sample statistics are used to test theories in much the same way that cases are tried in court. A defendant is charged with an offence, and there is an initial assumption of innocence. It is expected that the evidence will be consistent with this assumption. But if the evidence reveals facts that are unlikely to have occurred on the basis of innocence, the defendant is asserted to be guilty.

In statistics, the theory to be tested is called the **null hypothesis** (**H_0**). The null hypothesis will state something like 'the population mean is 25'. At the outset it is assumed that the null hypothesis is true. This gives rise to an expectation that, when a random sample is drawn, the sample mean will be close to 25. When the sample is observed, it may happen that the sample mean is a long way from 25. This would be unlikely to occur if the null hypothesis were true. On that basis, the null hypothesis would be rejected in favour of the **alternative hypothesis** (**H_1**).

Notice that the key question is: 'What is the probability of the data, assuming that the null hypothesis is true?' This probability is called the **p-value**, or simply '**p**'. If **p** is small, the null hypothesis is rejected. If **p** $<$ 5%, we say that the evidence against the null hypothesis is **significant**. The 5% significance level will be used throughout this book. Other common levels of significance are 1% ('very significant') and 0.1% ('highly significant').

It is possible for a miscarriage of justice to occur. A null hypothesis may be rejected even though it is true, simply because an unfortunate sample has been drawn. This is called a **type 1 error**. The probability of occurrence of a type 1 error is the level of significance (5%). This is sometimes called the **producer's risk**, α (alpha). The probability of occurrence of a **type 2 error** (accepting a false null hypothesis) is called the **consumer's risk**, β (beta).

In order to test the hypothesis that the mean weight of a bag of peanuts is 25 g, we write:

H_0: $\mu = 25$

A process engineer will be concerned if the bags of peanuts are either too heavy or too light, and will state the alternative hypothesis as follows:

H_1: $\mu \neq 25$

This is called a **vague alternative** hypothesis, because a departure from 25 in any direction will lead to rejection of the null hypothesis. This will lead to a **two-tailed test**. A consumer might be concerned only if the bags are too light, and will state the alternative hypothesis as follows:

H_1: $\mu < 25$

This is called a **specific alternative** hypothesis, because only a departure from 25 in a particular direction will lead to rejection of the null hypothesis. This will lead to a **one-tailed test**.

Hypothesis Testing Procedure

1. State $\mathbf{H_0}$ and $\mathbf{H_1}$.
2. Draw a random sample.
3. Compute the **test statistic** using the appropriate formula.
4. Use statistical tables to identify the **critical value**. This identifies the **rejection region**, which comprises one tail or two tails of the appropriate distribution, accounting for an area of 5%.
5. If the test statistic is in the rejection region then $\mathbf{p} < 5\%$, so reject $\mathbf{H_0}$. Otherwise, accept $\mathbf{H_0}$.

Alternatively, software can be used to calculate an exact **p**-value after steps 1 and 2 are performed.

Testing a Mean or Proportion

Testing a Mean

Formula 5.1

One-sample z-test

H_0: μ = some value

$$z = \frac{\overline{X} - \mu}{\sigma/\sqrt{n}}$$

Use **z** if σ is known.

Notice that the numerator in the **one-sample z-test** measures the difference between our observations (the sample mean) and our expectations (based on H_0). The denominator is the standard error, i.e. how big we would expect this difference to be. The test statistic therefore shows the scale of the disagreement between the evidence and the theory. The **p**-value measures exactly how likely it is that so much disagreement would happen by chance.

Example: Bags of peanuts are claimed to weigh 'not less than 25 g, on average'. It is known that the standard deviation of the bag weights is $\sigma = 3$ g. Test the claim, if a random sample of bags weighed as follows:

21, 22, 22, 26, 19, 22
H_0: $\mu = 25$; H_0 must state a single value for μ.
H_1: $\mu < 25$; this specific alternative hypothesis will lead to a one-tailed test, using the left tail, because it is 'less than'.
$\bar{X} = 22$
$n = 6$
$z = (22-25)/(3 / \sqrt{6}) = -2.449$
The tables identify critical $z = 1.645$ (i.e. t tables, final row, one-tailed). Since we are dealing with the left tail, critical $z = -1.645$. Any value more extreme than -1.645 is in the rejection region.
-2.449 is in the rejection region ($p < 5\%$).
Reject H_0: $\mu = 25$, in favour of H_1: $\mu < 25$
The claim is rejected, at the 5% level.

Formula 5.2

One-sample t-test
H_0: μ = some value

$$t = \frac{\bar{X} - \mu}{s/\sqrt{n}}$$

Use **t** if σ is unknown.

Usually the population standard deviation is unknown, and a **one-sample t-test** must be used. We repeat the previous example, without assuming any prior knowledge of σ.

Example: Bags of peanuts are claimed to weigh 'not less than 25 g, on average'. Test this claim, if a random sample of bags weighed as follows:
21, 22, 22, 26, 19, 22
H_0: $\mu = 25$
H_1: $\mu < 25$

$\overline{X} = 22$
$s = 2.28$
$n = 6$
$df = 5$
$t = (22-25)/(2.28 / \sqrt{6}) = -3.22$
The tables identify critical $t = -2.015$
-3.22 is in the rejection region ($p < 5\%$).
Reject H_0: $\mu = 25$, in favour of H_1: $\mu < 25$
The claim is rejected, at the 5% level.

The one-sample **t**-test can also be used with paired data to test the hypothesis that the mean difference is zero.

Example: Grace used a titration method to measure the vitamin C concentration of peppers. The data below show the results for peppers stored in the fridge, and for similar peppers stored at room temperature. Do the data assert that storage condition makes any difference to vitamin C concentration?

Table 5.1

Item	Fridge	Room Temperature
Green Pepper	40.2	35.5
Yellow Pepper	34.7	31.6
Orange Pepper	31.5	27.3
Red Pepper	30.2	21.8

H_0: $\mu = 0$, i.e. mean difference is zero.
H_1: $\mu \neq 0$, a vague alternative, 'any difference', two-tailed test.
Differences: 4.7, 3.1, 4.2, 8.4
$\overline{X} = 5.1$
$s = 2.30$
$n = 4$
$df = 3$
$t = (5.1 - 0)/(2.30 / \sqrt{4}) = 4.43$
The tables identify critical $t = 3.182$
4.43 is in the rejection region ($p < 5\%$).
Reject H_0: $\mu = 0$, in favour of H_1: $\mu \neq 0$
The null hypothesis is rejected, at the 5% level.

Storage conditions do make a difference. Vitamin C content is higher for peppers stored in the fridge.

Testing a Proportion

By counting the number of units in a random sample that possess some attribute, a judgment can be made about the population proportion, using a **one-sample P-test**. This allows an assessment to be made of political opinions, production reject rates, etc.

Formula 5.3

One-sample P-test

H_0: π = some value

$$z = \frac{P-\pi}{\sqrt{\frac{\pi(1-\pi)}{n}}}$$

Conditions: $n\pi \geq 5$ and $n.(1-\pi) \geq 5$.

Example: A supplier of tubes signed a contract to supply goods that are 'not more than 8% defective on average'. A random sample of 315 tubes included 30 defective tubes. Can it be asserted that the contract has been violated?

H_0: $\pi = 0.08$

H_1: $\pi > 0.08$

n = 315

P = 30/315 = 0.095

z = (0.095 − 0.08) / √(0.08 × 0.92/315) = 0.98

Critical **z** = 1.645

0.98 is not in the rejection region.

Accept **H_0**.

The data do not assert, at the 5% level, that the contract has been violated.

Problems 5.1

1. The average weight of glue beads is thought to be 5 grams. The standard deviation is known to be 0.15 grams. The weights, in grams, of a random sample of 5 of these beads are shown below. Do these data contradict the theory?
   4.92, 5.06, 4.88, 4.79, 4.93
2. The weights of chocolate bars are described as 'average not less than 50 g'. The standard deviation of the weights is 0.5 g. Does the following sample of weights challenge the description above?
   49.76, 49.72, 50.13, 50.04, 49.54, 49.72
3. The mean annual rainfall in a certain area is believed to be 80 mm. Test the theory at the 5% level, using the following random sample of annual rainfall data.
   75, 81, 72, 75, 69, 63, 70, 72

4. The fuel consumption of five vehicles, in litres per 100 km, was measured before servicing, and again afterwards. Can it be asserted that fuel consumption tends to be lower after servicing?

Table 5.2

Driver	Before	After
Matthew	13	12
Thomas	15	13
Princewill	16	14
Evan	15	15
Gino	14	13

5. Seven workers attended a course aimed at improving their typing speeds. Their speeds, in words per minute, before and after the course, are shown below. Is the course generally effective?

Table 5.3

Worker	Before	After
Pauline	23	25
Peggy	37	37
Paddy	39	43
James	45	50
John	46	45
Marian	39	46
Tom	51	54

6. Out of 220 people on the Galway–Dublin train, 92 were travelling for business reasons. Can we be sure that less than half travel for business?
7. A botanist predicted that one in four laburnum trees would have pink flowers. Out of 96 trees observed, only 15 had pink flowers. Is this consistent with the botanist's prediction?

Difference between Means or Proportions

One of the most common questions in statistics is whether two populations are different in respect to some measurement or attribute. Do teak window frames last longer than pine window frames? Is Gary more likely than Gareth to score a penalty? A choice between alternatives is often based on the insight provided by sample data.

Difference between Means

Formula 5.4

Two-sample t-test

$H_0: \mu_1 = \mu_2$

$$t = \frac{\bar{X}_1 - \bar{X}_2}{\sqrt{s^2/n_1 + s^2/n_2}}$$

s^2 is the pooled variance estimate, assuming equal variances.

Example: The following measurements of 'biological oxygen demand' were taken from the influent and effluent of a groundwater treatment tank. A **two-sample t-test** can be used to investigate whether the effluent measurements are lower.

Influent: 220, 198, 198

Effluent: 186, 180, 180, 174, 177, 165, 174, 171

$H_0: \mu_1 = \mu_2$

$H_1: \mu_1 > \mu_2$

$n_1 = 3$

$n_2 = 8$

$s_1 = 12.70$

$s_2 = 6.40$

$s^2 = 67.73$, pooled variance estimate using formula 4.10

$df = 9$

$\bar{X}_1 = 205.33$

$\bar{X}_2 = 175.88$

$t = (205.33-175.88)/\sqrt{(67.73/3 + 67.73/8)} = 5.29$

The tables identify critical $t = 1.833$

5.29 is in the rejection region ($p < 5\%$).

Reject $H_0: \mu_1 = \mu_2$, in favour of $H_1: \mu_1 > \mu_2$

The data assert that the effluent measurements are lower.

Difference between Proportions

Differences between proportions can be tested by counting the data and presenting a summary in a table. The table below summarises the quality of flowers sampled from two suppliers.

Table 5.4

	OK	Defective
Ben	177	23
Dylan	252	48

In this example, the rows represent the two populations (suppliers) and the columns represent the outcomes. We wish to know whether the outcome is contingent (i.e. dependent) on the row, so the table is called a **contingency table**. This can also be called a test of association, because we are investigating whether there is an association between outcome and supplier.

Formula 5.5

Contingency Tables

H_0: No association exists between the row and column categories.

$$\chi^2 = \sum \frac{(O-E)^2}{E}$$

O is the observed frequency and **E** the expected frequency.
E = row total × column total ÷ grand total
Condition: Every **E** ≥ 5
df = (rows −1) × (columns −1)

H_0: No association exists between supplier and quality.
First, the marginal totals are computed. Notice that the initial table did not display the totals, but simply the counts within each cell. Next, the expected frequencies are calculated and displayed below the observed frequencies.

Table 5.5

	OK	Defective	Totals
Ben	177 171.6	23 28.4	200
Dylan	252 257.4	48 42.6	300
Totals	429	71	500

In the first cell, **E** = 200 × 429 / 500 = 171.6
E is calculated for every cell.
The χ^2 contributions from all the cells are calculated and summed.
$\chi^2 = (177-171.6)^2/171.6 + (23-28.4)^2/28.4$
$+ (252-257.4)^2/257.4 + (48-42.6)^2/42.6$
$\chi^2 = 0.170 + 1.027$
$+ 0.113 + 0.685$
$\chi^2 = 1.994$
df = $(2-1)\times(2-1) = 1$
Critical $\chi^2 = 3.841$
We use the upper tail of the distribution, because we wish to know whether the observed and expected frequencies are significantly different, not whether they are significantly similar.
1.994 is not in the rejection region.
Accept $\mathbf{H}_0$.

The data do not establish, at the 5% level, that any difference exists between the proportions of defective flowers supplied by the two suppliers.

Tests of Association

A **test of association** can be used to compare proportions in any number of populations, not just two. In fact, a contingency table with any number of rows and any number of columns can be used to test for association between the row categories and the column categories.

Example: The numbers of male and female students, on courses in Computing, Science and Engineering, were observed. Is there an association between gender and course?

Table 5.6

	Computing	Science	Engineering
Male	20	17	44
Female	19	45	4

$\mathbf{H}_0$: No association exists between gender and course.
Compute the marginal totals and the expected frequencies.

Table 5.7

	Computing	Science	Engineering	Totals
Male	20 21.20	17 33.70	44 26.09	81
Female	19 17.80	45 28.30	4 21.91	68
Totals	39	62	48	149

In the first cell, $E = 81 \times 39 / 149 = 21.20$
Calculate E for every cell.
$\chi^2 = (20-21.20)^2/21.20 + (17-33.70)^2/33.70 + (44-26.09)^2/26.09$
$+ (19-17.80)^2/17.80 + (45-28.30)^2/28.30 + (4-21.91)^2/21.91$
$\chi^2 = 0.068 + 8.279 + 12.287 + 0.081 + 9.862 + 14.636$
$\chi^2 = 45.214$
df $= (2-1)\times(3-1) = 2$
Critical $\chi^2 = 5.991$
45.214 is in the rejection region ($p < 5\%$).
Reject $\mathbf{H}_0$.

The data assert that an association does exist between gender and course. There are fewer females on engineering courses compared to other courses.
When collecting data for a test of association, there are three equally valid options:

1. Collect a single random sample from the population, and classify every observation into the appropriate row and column.
2. Collect a random sample from each row, and classify every observation into the appropriate column.
3. Collect a random sample from each column, and classify every observation into the appropriate row.

Options 2 and 3 can be used to ensure sufficient representation of sparse categories, e.g. if there are only a small number of computing students in the college, we can ensure that we have sufficient numbers of computing students by deciding to sample a certain number of students from each course (option 3). If the expected values in some cells are still too small, we can decide to combine categories, e.g. reclassify the columns as ‘Engineering’ and ‘Other’. The advantage of option 1 is that we can also use the data to estimate the proportion of the population that belongs in any row or column category.

Selection Table for Tests

To select the appropriate test out of those presented so far, use this **selection table for tests**. Enter the column according to the type of data, and go to the row that corresponds to the number of populations being considered.

Table 5.8

	Measurements	Attributes
1 Population	One-sample **z**-test, if σ is known Or One-sample **t**-test, if σ is unknown	One-sample **P**-test
2 Populations	Paired **t**-test, if pairing is possible Or Two-sample **t**-test otherwise	Contingency Table
More than 2	One-Way ANOVA (see Chapter 6)	Contingency Table

PROBLEMS 5.2

1. Liam weighed himself three times in succession on a scale and the readings, in kg, were: 25.4, 25.6, 24.9. Sean weighed himself twice on the same scale and his results were: 31.2, 31.9. Do these data assert that Sean is heavier?
2. An industrial process fills cartridges with ink. At 10 a.m. a sample of fills were measured, with the following results, in ml: 55, 49, 57, 48, 52. At 11 a.m. another sample was taken: 53, 59, 50, 49, 52. Do these data assert that the process mean has changed?
3. Of a sample of 150 patrons at a theme park in summer, 15 had prepaid tickets. Of a sample of 800 patrons at the theme park in winter, only 9 had prepaid tickets. Do these data assert that the population proportions are different?
4. Broken biscuits are occasionally noticed in boxes awaiting shipment. A sample of 100 boxes packed by hand included 3 boxes with some broken biscuits. A sample of 100 boxes packed by machine included 17 boxes with some broken biscuits. Do these data indicate that the problem is related to the packing method?

5. A mobile communications provider has two types of customer: Prepaid and Bill. Occasionally, complaints are received from customers and these are categorised as relating to the customer's Handset, Network or Account. A random sample taken from the complaints database is tabulated below. Do these data indicate that different types of customer tend to have different complaints?

Table 5.9

	Handset	Network	Account
Prepaid	15	2	4
Bill	35	48	46

Sample Size and Power

'How big should my sample be?' is an important question to ask when testing a theory. If the **sample size** is too small, it may not contain sufficient evidence to reject a false null hypothesis. Such a test lacks **power**. Power is the probability of correctly rejecting the null hypothesis when it is false.

Asking the question, 'How big should my sample be?' is like asking the question, 'How long must I spend searching for a needle in a haystack?' The answer depends on three things: 1. How small is the needle? 2. How big is the haystack? 3. What chance do you want to have of finding the needle?

In statistical hypothesis testing, the corresponding issues are:

1. Delta: In a hypothesis test, we look for a difference between the hypothesised value of a parameter and its actual value. We must decide on the minimum difference, **delta**, which is of practical importance. For example, if I investigate the difference between the average annual running costs of my current heating system and an alternative system, I may decide that unless the alternative system costs €200 less per annum, it is not worth the trouble of making the changeover. Note that this is a practical decision and not a statistical one. The smaller the value of delta, the larger the sample size will be.

2. Sigma: This is the standard deviation of the population, which may be known from previous experience or estimated from a pilot sample. In the case of attribute data, the standard deviation of a sample proportion depends on the population proportion, so either this can be estimated, or the most conservative value, namely 0.5, can be used. The larger the value of sigma, the larger the sample size will be.

3. Power: As a rule of thumb we select a power of 80% for detecting a difference of size delta. This gives a good chance of detecting a practically significant difference if one exists. We could use the word **research** to refer to this activity of looking for a difference. On other occasions, our objective is to prove that there is no difference. We call this **validation**. We are trying to make an assertion of innocence, rather than an assumption of innocence. This requires a larger sample size, which can be achieved by selecting a power of 95% for detecting a difference of size delta. This has the effect of putting the 5% onus of proof on the null hypothesis rather than the alternative hypothesis. If this larger sample is unable to reject the null hypothesis, then we are no longer assuming it to be true: the data have asserted it to be true. In summary, a power of 80% is recommended for research, and 95% for validation.

Having identified the values of delta, sigma and power, a statistical software package can be used to compute the required sample size. It is also necessary to specify whether a one-tailed or two-tailed test is proposed: a one-tailed test requires a smaller sample size. If the sample size has already been decided, the power can be calculated instead. Whenever a hypothesis test leads to the null hypothesis being accepted, it is worth asking what the power of the test was. If the power was low, the conclusion does not tell us much.

Tests of Variances and Goodness-of-fit

One-sample Variance Test

The **chi-square** distribution is used to test a hypothesis concerning a population variance. Since the distribution is asymmetric, the upper 5% point of the distribution is used for a 'greater than' alternative, and the lower 5% point (the upper 95% point) for a 'less than' alternative. For a 'not equal to' alternative, the upper 2.5% and 97.5% points are used to identify the rejection region.

Formula 5.6

One-sample Variance Test

H_0: σ^2 = some value

$$\chi^2 = \frac{(n-1)s^2}{\sigma^2}$$

Condition: A normal population.

Example: The diameters of bagels are required to have a standard deviation of 2 mm or less. It is assumed that the bagels currently being produced conform to this requirement. Do the sample data below assert otherwise?

Diameters in mm: 97, 94, 96, 95, 99, 93

H_0: $\sigma^2 = 4$; the test uses the variance, not the standard deviation

H_1: $\sigma^2 > 4$

n = 6

s = 2.16

$\chi^2 = (6-1) \times 2.16^2 / 4$

$\chi^2 = 5.832$

df = 5

Critical χ^2 = 11.070

5.832 is not in the rejection region.

Accept H_0.

No, these data do not assert, at the 5% level, that the standard deviation is greater than 2 mm.

Two-sample Variance Test

If two samples are drawn from normal populations, the ratio of the sample variances follows an **F** distribution. We define the **F-statistic** as the ratio of the larger sample variance to the smaller one, and this always leads to a one-tailed test, using the upper 5% point of the **F** distribution. The **F** distribution has degrees of freedom for the numerator and denominator, in that order.

Formula 5.7

Two-sample Variance Test

H_0: $\sigma_1^2 = \sigma_2^2$

$$F = \frac{s_1^2}{s_2^2} \quad \text{where } s_1^2 \geq s_2^2$$

Condition: Normal populations.

df = $n_1 - 1$, $n_2 - 1$ (numerator df, denominator df)

Example: The thicknesses of paint specimens applied by brush and by sprayer were measured, in microns. Do these data indicate that the thickness is equally consistent for the two modes of application?

Brush: 270, 295, 315, 249, 296, 340

Sprayer: 325, 333, 341, 334, 317, 342, 339, 321

H_0: $\sigma_1^2 = \sigma_2^2$

$n_1 = 6$

$n_2 = 8$

$s_1 = 32.13$

$s_2 = 9.47$

F = 11.51

df = 5,7

Critical **F** = 3.972

11.51 is in the rejection region ($p < 5\%$).

Reject H_0.

The data assert that sprayed paint exhibits less variation in thickness than brushed paint.

Test of Goodness-of-fit

We may wish to test the **goodness-of-fit** of some data to a particular distribution, e.g. a Poisson distribution. This may sound like a rather academic exercise, but in fact it is one of the most interesting of all hypothesis tests. If we find that the Poisson distribution is not a good fit to data on the number of breakdowns that occur on a photocopier, for example, this indicates that the assumptions which apply to the Poisson distribution do not apply to that situation. The Poisson distribution assumes that events occur at random. If the Poisson distribution is not a good fit, then the events do not occur at random: perhaps they occur at regular intervals (i.e. uniform, like a 'dripping tap'), or perhaps they occur in clusters (i.e. contagious, 'it never rains but it pours'). This gives us useful information which may enable us to prevent future breakdowns. If the breakdowns occur at regular intervals, they may be caused by wear-out of some component: this could be addressed by scheduling regular servicing or replacement of that part. If the breakdowns occur in clusters, it may indicate that the remedy being applied is ineffective, so a new repair strategy needs to be devised.

This is just one example. The interpretation will vary greatly from case to case. The set of problems which follow this section will provide opportunity for thinking through the practical implications of statistical conclusions.

Formula 5.8

χ^2 Goodness-of-fit Test

H_0: The population has some specified distribution

$$\chi^2 = \sum \frac{(O-E)^2}{E}$$

O is the observed frequency and **E** the expected frequency in each of the **k** categories.

Conditions: (i) **k** ≥ 5

(ii) Every **E** ≥ 1 (adjacent categories may be combined to achieve this).

df = **k** – **j** – 1, where **j** is the number of parameters estimated from the data.

Example: A die was rolled 30 times. The outcomes are summarised below. Is it a fair die?

Table 5.10

Outcome	1	2	3	4	5	6
Frequency	6	3	5	8	5	3

$\mathbf{H_0}$: The population has a uniform distribution with $\mathbf{k} = 6$.
There were a total of 30 rolls, so the expected frequencies are: 5, 5, 5, 5, 5, 5
$\chi^2 = (6-5)^2/5 + (3-5)^2/5 + (5-5)^2/5 + (8-5)^2/5 + (5-5)^2/5 + (3-5)^2/5$
$\chi^2 = 1/5 + 4/5 + 0/5 + 9/5 + 0/5 + 4/5 = 3.6$
$\mathbf{df} = 6-0-1 = 5$ (No parameters were estimated from the data.)
Critical value of $\chi^2 = 11.070$
3.6 is not in the rejection region.
Accept $\mathbf{H_0}$.

The data are consistent with the assumption that the die is fair. We cannot assert that the die is 'weighted' in favour of some numbers at the expense of others.

Having completed this chapter you should be able to:

- identify the statistical test that corresponds to a practical question;
- perform a hypothesis test and interpret the result;
- appreciate the implications of sample size and power.

Problems 5.3

1. A process that fills masses of powder into capsules has a standard deviation of 5 mg. A new process has been tried out and the masses of nine quantities of powder filled by this process are shown. Do the data assert that the new process is less variable?
   Mass in mg: 251, 255, 252, 250, 254, 253, 253, 251, 252
2. A pharmaceutical producer has manufacturing sites in Ireland and in India. Engineers at each site, working independently, have each devised a dynamic method for the measurement of compressed tablet height. Each method was tested by taking a single tablet and recording a number of repeat measurements. Do the results below assert that either method is more precise?
   Ireland: 4.0, 3.6, 3.6, 4.0, 3.3
   India: 3.5, 3.6, 3.7, 3.4, 3.7
3. Two engineering firms, Japanese and American, supplied similar gearbox components to an automotive manufacturer. A sample of components was taken from each supplier and the diameters were measured, in mm. Is there significant evidence of a difference in precision?
   Japan: 12.51, 12.48, 12.51, 12.50, 12.51, 12.52

USA: 12.50, 12.50, 12.48, 12.51

4. A group of 29 students were each asked to choose a random digit between 0 and 9 inclusive. Do the data, summarised in this frequency table, appear to come from a uniform distribution?

Table 5.11

Digit	0	1	2	3	4	5	6	7	8	9
Students	1	2	0	4	4	7	3	6	2	0

5. One Saturday, the number of goals scored in each of the 56 matches played in the English and Scottish leagues was recorded. Is the Poisson distribution a good fit? Do goals behave like 'accidents'? Goalkeepers might say yes, goal-scorers might say no: but what do the data say?

Table 5.12

Goals	0	1	2	3	4	5	6	7	8
Matches	6	13	15	12	5	1	1	2	1

6. A consignment of eggs was found to contain a large number of cracked eggs. Before disposing of the consignment, the number of cracked eggs in each carton (of 6) was counted. Is the binomial distribution a good fit? Did the damage occur before or after the eggs were packed into the cartons?

Table 5.13

Cracked	0	1	2	3	4	5	6
Cartons	80	14	12	20	16	21	40

7. (Project) Design and carry out a test of association on any population of your choice, using a contingency table, and write a report in the following format.
   (a) Describe the population of interest and the purpose of your study.
   (b) Explain how you sampled from the population, and why you chose this particular sampling scheme.
   (c) Display the table of observed and expected frequencies, and present the analysis.
   (d) Are the categories associated? State your conclusions simply and completely, without using any statistical jargon.
   (e) Suggest two possible causes of association between the categories you have studied.

6
EXPERIMENTS

At the end of this chapter you will be able to:

- design experiments involving one or more factors;
- analyse experimental data and summarise the findings;
- use designed experiments to identify causes and improve processes.

The purpose of an experiment is to discover information. This information may provide insight leading to action that will improve a process. An experiment must be designed properly so that it will:

1. capture the right kind of information;
2. capture a sufficient amount of information; and
3. not mix this information up with something else.

Typically an experiment will consider the effect of a **factor** on a **response**. For example, we might want to investigate the effect of different players on the distance a football is kicked. The response (distance) is what we measure in the experiment. The factor (player) is what we change, to see how it will affect the response. In the experiment, a number of different players (**factor levels**) are studied. Notice that we are not just watching a game as spectators: we decide who kicks the ball, in what order, and how often. This is an **experiment**, and not an **observational study**. In an observational study we become familiar with the behaviour of a process, and so we can describe or predict its behaviour. But in an experiment we set out to identify causes, and this may enable us to change the behaviour of the process.

Single-Factor Experiments: Design and ANOVA

A single-factor experiment considers the effect of one factor on a response, e.g. the effect of player on distance. Any other factors that could affect the distance, such as the type of ball used, are deliberately excluded from the experiment.

But what about things like the weather? Small, uncontrollable changes in the environment will cause minor fluctuations in the measured response, even when the factor level remains unchanged. It is important to design every experiment in a way that takes account of these issues, by applying the following principles.

Principles of Experimental Design

Replication

We measure the response more than once for each factor level. This allows us to see how much the response varies even when the factor level remains the same. We call this the error variance. The word 'error' does not denote a mistake of any kind: it simply acknowledges that there are many small influences that cannot be eliminated, such as the exact state of the weather, the grass, the ball, the player, etc. Later on we will consider exactly how many replicates are required: for now we will simply note that one observation is not enough.

Randomisation

We randomise the order in which the experimental **runs** are performed. We do not allow Damien to perform all his kicks first, followed by Jessy and finally Wayne. There may be some progressive deterioration in the conditions, and that would place Wayne at a disadvantage. Instead, we make a list of all the runs to be performed and then we use a random-number generator to determine the **run order**.

If a different **experimental unit** (ball) must be used for each run, then the **allocation** of the experimental units is also randomised. We do not give the first footballs we find to Damien, and so on, because the first ones may be older or heavier or different in some other way.

Blocking

Suppose the number of replicates is so great that we require two days to complete the experiment. There could be some difference between the two days that would affect the responses. Then instead of fully randomising the runs across the two days, we regard each day as a **block**, and within each block we make sure to allocate an equal number of runs to each factor level. So if each player has to perform 30 kicks, they could each do 20 kicks on the first day and 10 kicks on the second day. A block is a subset of the experimental units, which are believed to be similar in responsiveness, but which may differ in responsiveness from the units in another block. Typical blocks are: in manufacturing – batches; in clinical trials – gender; in measurement systems – days. We will not mention blocks again until we come to deal with two-factor experiments.

Structuring your Data

A recording form can be used to display the experimental design and then to record the measurements as they arise. Notice that all the measurements are stacked in a single column. There is a column (with a sensible title) for every variable, and a row for every case. This is the best way to structure data, and it also facilitates the use of software.

In this table, a column of random numbers was generated, and these were ranked to determine the run order. When software is used to create the design, the entire table is usually sorted into run order and the random numbers are not displayed.

Table 6.1

Player	Random No.	Run Order	Distance
Damien	0.368843	5	45
Jessy	0.738684	9	48
Wayne	0.474818	7	43
Damien	0.928478	12	42
Jessy	0.534303	8	50
Wayne	0.212354	2	41
Damien	0.882270	10	46
Jessy	0.437575	6	47
Wayne	0.159179	1	43
Damien	0.890182	11	48
Jessy	0.248853	3	52
Wayne	0.272851	4	48

The question of interest is: Does the factor (player) have an effect on the response (distance)?

Hypotheses and Models

The null hypothesis (**H_0**) states that the factor has no effect on the response. This is equivalent to saying that the population means are equal for all the factor levels. According to the null hypothesis, there is only random variation present, and the response could be described by the following **model**. (Note: Although a model looks like a formula, we do not use a model to 'get the answer', but rather to express a relationship that may exist between variables.)

Model 6.1

Model with Random Variation Only

$$Y_i = \mu + \epsilon_i$$

In this generic model, **Y** represents the response on occasion **i**, **μ** represents the average response, and ϵ represents the random error on that occasion. In our football example, **Y** represents how far the ball was kicked on occasion **i**, **μ** represents the average distance the ball is kicked, and ϵ represents how much further the ball travelled compared to the average on that occasion.

The alternative hypothesis (**H_1**) states that the factor does have an effect on the response. If this is so, then some of the variation in the response is explained by the factor and so the complete model is as follows.

Model 6.2

Model for One Factor

$Y_{ij} = \mu + \alpha_i + \epsilon_{ij}$

In this generic model, **Y** represents the response to factor level **i** on occasion **j**, **μ** represents the grand average response, α represents the **effect** of factor level **i**, and ϵ represents the random error on that occasion. In our football example, **Y** represents how far the ball was kicked by person **i** on occasion **j**, **μ** represents the grand average distance the ball is kicked by all players, α represents how much the average distance for person **i** exceeds the grand average, and ϵ represents how much further the ball travelled on that occasion compared to the average distance for that person.

If the null hypothesis is correct, every $\alpha = 0$. If this is true, it does not matter who kicks the ball.

According to the alternative hypothesis, there are two sources of variation present: **explained variation** (α) and **unexplained variation** (ϵ). According to the alternative hypothesis, if you want to predict how far the ball will travel, it is useful to know who is kicking it. And if you want to control how far the ball will travel, you should choose a particular player to kick it.

Analysis of Variance (ANOVA)

We will now analyse the data from the experiment using **ANOVA** (ANalysis Of VAriance). As its name suggests, ANOVA involves looking at the data for evidence of every alleged source of variation. We begin by **unstacking** the data.

Table 6.2

Distance Damien	Distance Jessy	Distance Wayne
45	48	43
42	50	41
46	47	43
48	52	48

Next, we calculate the mean and variance of each sample.

Table 6.3

	Damien	Jessy	Wayne
Mean	45.250	49.250	43.750
Variance	2.50^2	2.217^2	2.986^2

Step 1: We look at the error variance first, i.e. how different are the distances when the same player is involved? The three sample variances 2.50^2, 2.217^2 and 2.986^2 all attempt to answer this question. Each of these variances is an estimate of the error variance, so it makes sense to combine them into a single 'pooled' estimate, by averaging them. The pooled estimate is $(2.50^2 + 2.217^2 + 2.986^2) / 3 = 6.69$, symbol s_w^2. This is the **pooled within-samples** variance, also called the error variance. Each of the individual estimates is based on $4-1$ degrees of freedom, so the pooled estimate has $3(4-1) = 9$ degrees of freedom.

Step 2: Next we look at variation due to the factor, i.e. how different are the distances when different players are involved? We can estimate this by calculating the variance between the sample means above. This **between-samples** variance is denoted by s_b^2. It is based on $3-1 = 2$ degrees of freedom. $s_b^2 = 2.843^2 = 8.083$. This figure needs to be adjusted because it is a variance of sample means, but the variance of individual values is bigger than this. Therefore, we multiply s_b^2 by 4, in order to estimate the variance between single distances for different players. We require $n \times s_b^2 = 4 \times 8.083 = 32.33$

Step 3: The central question is this: Is the factor having an effect on the response at all? Maybe not. Perhaps the apparent variation due to the factor is just more random variation. We can test this hypothesis by comparing the variance due to the factor with the variance due to error. To see if it is significantly bigger, we compute the variance ratio, F, which is named after Sir Ronald Fisher, who developed experimental design and ANOVA. $F = 32.33 / 6.69 = 4.83$.

Step 4: Finally, we consider whether the calculated value of F is so unusual that it could not have occurred by chance. From the tables of the F distribution, we see that the critical value of F, having 2 and 9 degrees of freedom, is 4.256. The calculated value of F exceeds this value, and therefore its p-value is less than 5%. We reject the null hypothesis, which states that the player has no effect on the distance. We say that the result is significant, i.e. the disagreement between the data and the null hypothesis is sufficiently great to lead to rejection of the null hypothesis. The data assert, at the 5% level, that the player does affect the distance.

The ANOVA procedure that we have followed is summarised by the formula below.

Formula 6.1

One-Way ANOVA

H_0: The factor has no effect on the response.

For **k** factor levels with **n** replications each, i.e. **k** samples of size **n**:

$$F = \frac{n.s_b^2}{s_w^2}$$

s_b^2 is the 'between-samples' variance

s_w^2 is the pooled 'within-samples' variance

df = k - 1, k(n - 1)

Assumptions: Errors are (1) independent and (2) normal, (3) with uniform variance.

What do the assumptions mean in our example?

1. The errors are independent. What this means is that if one of Damien's kicks is a short one for Damien, there is no reason to expect that his next kick will also be short. Damien is not being disadvantaged in any way, and neither is any other player. That is, the experiment is free from systematic bias. Randomisation will tend to ensure that this is true.
2. The errors are normally distributed. The population of Damien's distances is a normal distribution, and the same can be said for the other players' distances.
3. The errors have a uniform variance. The error variance does not depend on the factor level. Even though one player may kick the ball further on average than some other player, the variation in distances is the same for all players.

The first of these assumptions is crucial. The second and third assumptions are less important and ANOVA will still work quite well if these assumptions are violated. We say that ANOVA is **robust**.

Computer Output

If the data from our football experiment were analysed by software, the output would consist of an **ANOVA table** like this.

Table 6.4

One-way ANOVA: Distance versus Player

Source	DF	SS	MS	F	P
Player	2	64.67	32.33	4.83	0.038
Error	9	60.25	6.69		
Total	11	124.92			

The **p**-value is less than 5%, showing that the data were unlikely to arise on the basis of the assumption that player has no effect on distance. We therefore reject this null hypothesis in favour of the alternative: player does have an effect on distance.

Every ANOVA table has the same headings: **Source** (of variation), **DF** (degrees of freedom), **SS** ('sum of squares' of the deviations), **MS** ('mean square' deviation, i.e. variance), **F** (variance ratio), and **P** (the probability of obtaining the data if the factor has no effect on the response).

The software can also compute the estimated **fitted values** ($\mu+\alpha$) and **residuals** (the errors, ϵ).

Table 6.5

Player	Distance	Fits	Residuals
Damien	45	45.25	–0.25
Jessy	48	49.25	–1.25
Wayne	43	43.75	–0.75
Damien	42	45.25	–3.25
Jessy	50	49.25	0.75
Wayne	41	43.75	–2.75
Damien	46	45.25	0.75
Jessy	47	49.25	–2.25
Wayne	43	43.75	–0.75
Damien	48	45.25	2.75
Jessy	52	49.25	2.75
Wayne	48	43.75	4.25

The ANOVA assumptions can be tested by **residual analysis**: a histogram of the residuals should look approximately normal (assumption 2), and a plot of residuals versus fits should show the points forming a horizontal belt of roughly uniform width (assumption 3). The residuals can also be plotted against the run order to confirm that there was no time-related pattern.

Problems 6.1

1. Jody carried out an experiment to investigate whether the colour of a birthday candle affects the burning time, measured in seconds.

Table 6.6

GREEN	ORANGE	YELLOW
1109	1129	1031
1053	980	1067
1042	1010	940

(a) Write a model for the response, and explain what each term represents.
(b) State and test the null hypothesis, working by hand.
(c) Repeat the analysis using software.
(d) State your conclusions in simple language.

2. Anne carried out an experiment to investigate whether the supermarket of origin affects the weights of clementines (measured in grams).

Table 6.7

TESCO	DUNNES
102	90
118	80
124	64
127	95
117	75

(a) Write a model for the response, and explain what each term represents.
(b) State and test the null hypothesis, working by hand.
(c) Repeat the analysis using software.
(d) State your conclusions in simple language.

3. (Exercise) Design and carry out an experiment to investigate the effect of style on the distance travelled by a paper aeroplane. Five aeroplanes should be made in each of two different styles. One person should throw all the aeroplanes, in random order. If the aeroplanes are thrown over a tiled floor, the distance can be measured by counting the number of tiles travelled. Analyse the results using one-way ANOVA.

4. (Project) Design a single-factor experiment, carry it out and analyse the results. You may choose any area of application: a business or industrial process, an area of academic interest, a sporting activity, or everyday life. Make sure that you have the authority to set the factor levels, and that you have a suitable instrument for measuring the response. Your report must consist of the following sections.
(a) State the purpose of your experiment, and explain the role of randomisation in your experiment.
(b) Write a model for the response in your experiment, and carefully explain what each term in the model represents.
(c) Display the data and the ANOVA table.
(d) Express the experimental findings in simple language.

Two-factor Experiments and Interaction

A two-factor experiment considers the effect of two factors on a response, e.g. the effect of driver and vehicle on fuel economy. There are two drivers (Jeremy and Ralph) and three vehicles (hatchback, saloon and SUV). Fuel economy is measured in litres/100 km.

This experiment will allow us to determine whether driver has an effect on fuel economy, and if vehicle has an effect on fuel economy. We are getting two experiments for the price of one! This is one of the advantages of including more than one factor in an experiment.

It is convenient to think about the experiment by using a table, in which the rows represent the levels of one factor, the columns represent the levels of the other factor, and each cell represents a particular **factor-level combination**. This is referred to as a **crossed design** because every level of one factor is crossed (i.e. combined with) every level of the other factor. It does not matter which factor goes in the rows, and which one goes in the columns.

Table 6.8

	Hatchback	Saloon	SUV
Jeremy	6.2	6.5	8.1
Ralph	6.7	6.4	7.9

The number of entries in each cell indicates the level of replication. It is possible to do a limited analysis with only one observation per cell, as in this case, because although there is no replication in the cells, there is replication in the rows and the columns.
The response in an experiment like this can be modelled as follows:

Model 6.3

Additive Model for Two Factors

$$Y_{ij} = \mu + \alpha_i + \beta_j + \epsilon_{ij}$$

μ is the grand average response, averaged over all rows and columns.
α is the row effect, i.e. how much the row average exceeds the grand average.
β is the column effect, i.e. how much the column average exceeds the grand average.
ϵ is the error, i.e. how much an observation in a cell exceeds what we expect; we expect $\mu+\alpha+\beta$.

In this particular experiment:

μ is the grand average fuel consumption, averaged over all drivers and vehicles.
α is the driver effect, i.e. how much more fuel than average that driver uses.
β is the vehicle effect, i.e. how much more fuel than average that vehicle uses.
ϵ is the error, i.e. how much more fuel was used on that occasion compared to what would be expected for that driver–vehicle combination.

There are two null hypotheses of interest, namely:
every $\alpha = 0$, i.e. factor 1 (driver) has no effect on the response (fuel consumption), and every $\beta = 0$ i.e. factor 2 (vehicle) has no effect on the response (fuel consumption).

The data must be presented to the software in a proper structure, with a column for every variable, and a row for every case, as shown below.

Table 6.9

Driver	Vehicle	Fuel Economy
Jeremy	Hatchback	6.2
Jeremy	Saloon	6.5
Jeremy	SUV	8.1
Ralph	Hatchback	6.7
Ralph	Saloon	6.4
Ralph	SUV	7.9

The ANOVA table is as follows:

Table 6.10

Two-way ANOVA: Fuel Economy versus Driver, Vehicle

Source	DF	SS	MS	F	P
Driver	1	0.00667	0.00667	0.09	0.789
Vehicle	2	3.20333	1.60167	22.35	0.043
Error	2	0.14333	0.07167		
Total	5	3.35333			

Notice that the p-value for driver is greater than 0.05, but the p-value for vehicle is less than 0.05. We accept the null hypothesis that driver has no effect on fuel economy, but we reject the null hypothesis that vehicle has no effect on fuel economy (SUVs use more fuel).

In this experiment, we may not have been interested in the driver effect. We may have included two drivers in the experiment simply because there was not enough time for one driver to perform all of the experimental runs. If so, the drivers are the blocks. A block is like an extra factor that we include in an experiment because we cannot avoid doing so.

Interaction

So far we have not considered a two-factor experiment with replication. The experiment below considers the effect of person and language on the time, in seconds, required to read a page from a novel. There are three levels of person (Samuel, Alice and Manuel) and two levels of language (English and Spanish).

Table 6.11

	Samuel	Alice	Manuel
English	159 163	157 153	326 307
Spanish	319 302	306 312	160 152

In this experiment, there is replication in the cells: each person reads more than one page in each language, so we can do a full analysis. Looking at the data in the table, you will notice that the situation is not straightforward. The simple question, 'Which language requires a longer reading time?' does not have a simple answer. The answer begins with, 'It depends on who is reading.'

The response in an experiment like this can be modelled as follows.

Model 6.4

Model for Two Factors with Interaction

$$Y_{ijk} = \mu+\alpha_i+\beta_j+\eta_{ij}+\epsilon_{ijk}$$

Y is an individual response in the table: it is the **k**th observation in the cell located in row **i** and column **j**.
μ is the grand average response, averaged over all rows and columns.
α is the row effect, i.e. how much the row average exceeds the grand average.
β is the column effect, i.e. how much the column average exceeds the grand average.
η is the **interaction** effect, i.e. how much the cell average exceeds what is expected. Based on the additive model we would expect the cell average to be $\mu + \alpha + \beta$.
ϵ is the error, i.e. how much that individual observation exceeds the cell average.

In this particular experiment:

Y is the reading time for language **i** and person **j** on the **k**th occasion.
μ is the grand average reading time, averaged over all languages and persons.
α is the language effect, i.e. how much more time on average is required for that language.
β is the person effect, i.e. how much more time on average is required by that person.
η is the interaction effect, i.e. how much more time on average is required for that particular language–person combination, compared to what would be expected.
ϵ is the error, i.e. how much more time was taken on that occasion, compared to the average time for that language–person combination.

There are three null hypotheses of interest, namely:

every $\eta = 0$, i.e. there are no unusual cells in the table (no particular factor–level combination gives an unusual response);

every $\alpha = 0$, i.e. there are no unusual rows in the table (factor 1 has no effect on the response); and

every $\beta = 0$, i.e. there are no unusual columns in the table (factor 2 has no effect on the response).

Table 6.12

Two-way ANOVA: Time versus Person, Language

Source	DF	SS	MS	F	P
Person	2	43.2	21.6	0.33	0.730
Language	1	6816.3	6816.3	104.60	0.000
Interaction	2	65010.2	32505.1	498.80	0.000
Error	6	391.0	65.2		
Total	11	72260.7			

The first thing to examine in the ANOVA table is the interaction **p**-value. In this case, the interaction **p**-value is less than 0.05, so we conclude that there is an interaction effect. Interaction means that the effect of a particular factor depends on the level of some other factor. So when the question is asked, 'Which language requires a longer reading time?' the answer begins with 'It depends on which person is reading.' English requires more time if Manuel is reading, but Spanish requires more time if Samuel or Alice is reading. This can be illustrated using an **interaction plot**.

Fig 6.1

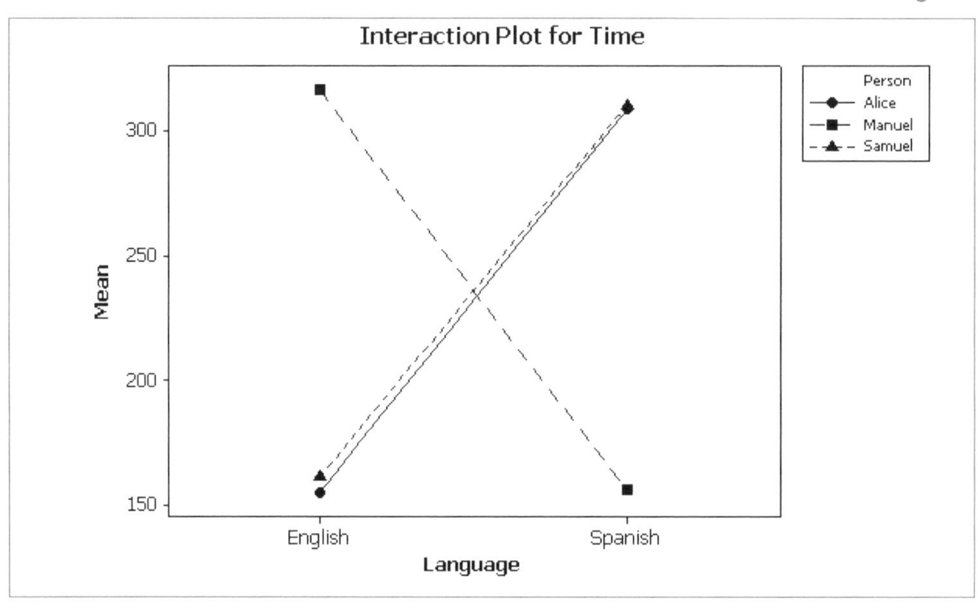

If there is no significant evidence of interaction in an ANOVA table, then we simply go ahead and interpret the p-values for the **main effects** in the usual way. But if there is interaction, we cannot trust the other p-values. For example, the p-value for language seems to indicate that some language takes longer to read than another. But the interaction p-value has warned us that the effect of language depends on the level of person. For this reason, interaction must always be investigated first.

Different kinds of interaction could arise. In the example above, some people took longer to read in English and others took longer in Spanish. With a different set of people, it could happen that all of them require extra time to read in Spanish, but the amount of extra time required could vary from person to person. This is also classed as interaction. However, if everyone requires the same amount of extra time to read in Spanish, that is not interaction: it is a language main effect. An interaction is like an allergic reaction that occurs with a particular person–food combination. In general, that person is healthy. In general, that food does not cause problems. The unusual effect is observed only when the two combine. In the same way, we say that interaction is present if some factor–level combination gives rise to an unexpected average response.

It should now be apparent that a major advantage of two-factor experiments is that interactions can be discovered. In single-factor experiments, interactions cannot be discovered.

Problems 6.2

1. An insurance office has three sales desks: one each for life, home, and motor insurance. Three sales clerks each spend some days at each desk. The daily sales revenue for each desk–clerk combination was recorded for a random sample of six days each. What can we learn from the analysis below?

Table 6.13

Two-way ANOVA: Revenue versus Clerk, Desk

Source	DF	SS	MS	F	P
Clerk	2	508338	254169	3.18	0.051
Desk	2	37226441	18613221	232.61	0.000
Interaction	4	358169	89542	1.12	0.359
Error	45	3600912	80020		
Total	53	41693860			

2. Ken carried out an experiment to investigate the effect of person and skate on the distance a skater is able to grind down a bar. Write a model for the response, analyse the data, and state conclusions simply.

Table 6.14

Person	Skate	Grind Distance
Ken	K1	1.3
Ken	K1	1.0
Norris	K1	0.8
Norris	K1	0.5
Rob	K1	1.0
Rob	K1	1.1
Ken	K2	1.0
Ken	K2	1.4
Norris	K2	1.2
Norris	K2	1.3
Rob	K2	1.7
Rob	K2	1.5
Ken	Fats	2.0
Ken	Fats	1.9
Norris	Fats	1.9
Norris	Fats	1.9
Rob	Fats	2.5
Rob	Fats	2.0

3. Aidan carried out an experiment to investigate the effect of person and pipette type on the measured volume of 5 ml of water. Write a model for the response, analyse the data, and state conclusions simply.

Table 6.15

Person	Pipette Type	Measured Volume
Anna	5	4.87
Anna	10	4.84
Evelyn	5	4.88
Evelyn	10	4.97
Ahmed	5	4.87
Ahmed	10	5.07
Anna	5	4.85
Anna	10	4.87
Evelyn	5	4.89
Evelyn	10	4.92
Ahmed	5	4.92
Ahmed	10	5.02

4. Darragh carried out an experiment to investigate the effect of guitar and method on the time required to play a scale. Write a model for the response, analyse the data, and state conclusions simply.

Table 6.16

Guitar	Method	Time
Nylon	Plectrum	9
Nylon	Plectrum	11
Nylon	Plectrum	8
Nylon	Plucking	9
Nylon	Plucking	10
Nylon	Plucking	8
Steel	Plectrum	7
Steel	Plectrum	7
Steel	Plectrum	7
Steel	Plucking	12
Steel	Plucking	11
Steel	Plucking	11

5. Justin carried out an experiment to investigate the effect of river and bait on the number of fish caught in a day. Write a model for the response, analyse the data, and state conclusions simply.

Table 6.17

River	Bait	Fish
Blackwater	Maggots	21
Blackwater	Maggots	11
Blackwater	Maggots	15
Blackwater	Maggots	23
Shannon	Maggots	30
Shannon	Maggots	24
Shannon	Maggots	31
Shannon	Maggots	27
Blackwater	Pellets	13
Blackwater	Pellets	11
Blackwater	Pellets	12
Blackwater	Pellets	13
Shannon	Pellets	19
Shannon	Pellets	18
Shannon	Pellets	16
Shannon	Pellets	18

6. (Exercise) Working with a colleague, design and carry out a two-factor experiment to investigate the effect of person (two levels: you and your colleague) and hand (two levels: left and right) on writing speed. Allow three replicates. Measure the writing speed by recording how many letters from the following sentence can be written in a ten-second interval. Sentence: 'The quick brown fox jumps over the lazy dog.' Draw conclusions using an ANOVA table, illustrate them on an interaction plot, and share them with others who have also performed this exercise.
7. (Project) Design a two-factor experiment with replication, carry it out, analyse the results, and write a report consisting of the following sections.
   (a) State the purpose of your experiment, and explain the role of randomisation in your experiment.
   (b) Write a model for the response in your experiment, and carefully explain what each term in the model represents.
   (c) Display the data and the ANOVA table.
   (d) Show one interaction plot.
   (e) Express the experimental findings in simple language.

Multi-Factor Experiments

We have seen that two-factor experiments have advantages over single-factor experiments: they are more economic, and interactions can be discovered. We can, of course, design a **multi-factor experiment**, which is even more efficient and informative. However, an experiment with many factors, each at many levels, will be a very large experiment. For example, a six-factor experiment, with 10 levels of each factor, requires one million experimental runs (10^6), not counting replication! Obviously we need to consider strategies to reduce the size of multi-factor experiments.

Strategy 1: Two-level Designs

Our first strategy is to investigate only two levels of every factor. Such experiments are called two-level **factorial experiments**, and for **k** factors they involve 2^k experimental runs. For example, a six-factor, two-level design will require 64 runs (2^6), not counting replication. The two levels of each factor are often referred to as high and low, or -1 and $+1$.

This short cut incurs a risk. By considering only two levels of every factor, there is a risk that **curvature** will go undetected. There may be a quadratic relationship between the response and one of the factors. Observing only two levels of the factor will not allow us to see this. Consider an experiment that investigates the effect of angle on the distance travelled by a paper aeroplane. With a ten-level design it is easy to see curvature in the response.

Fig 6.2

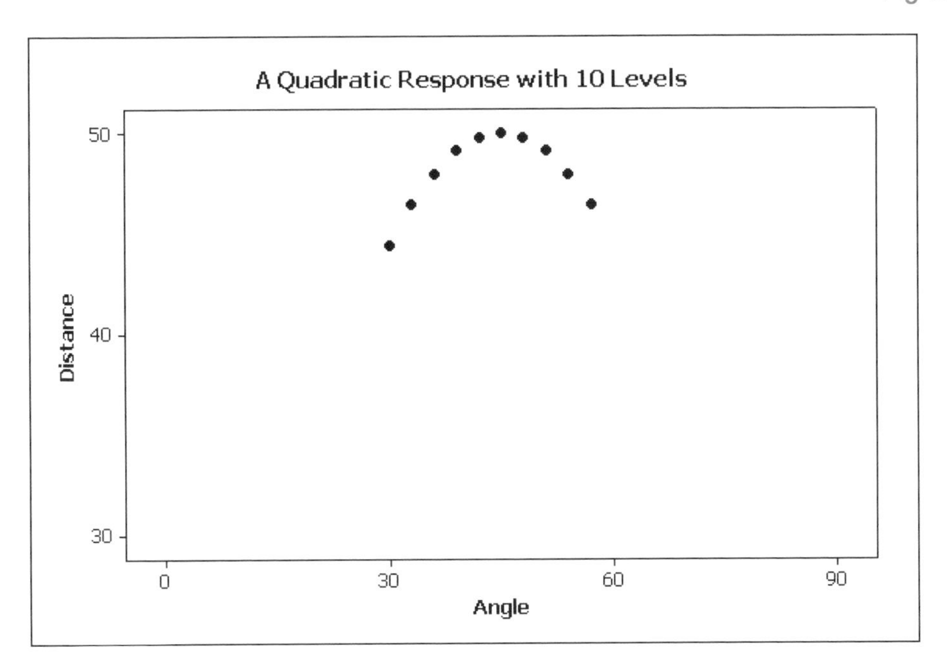

With a two-level design it is impossible to see that curvature is present.

Fig 6.3

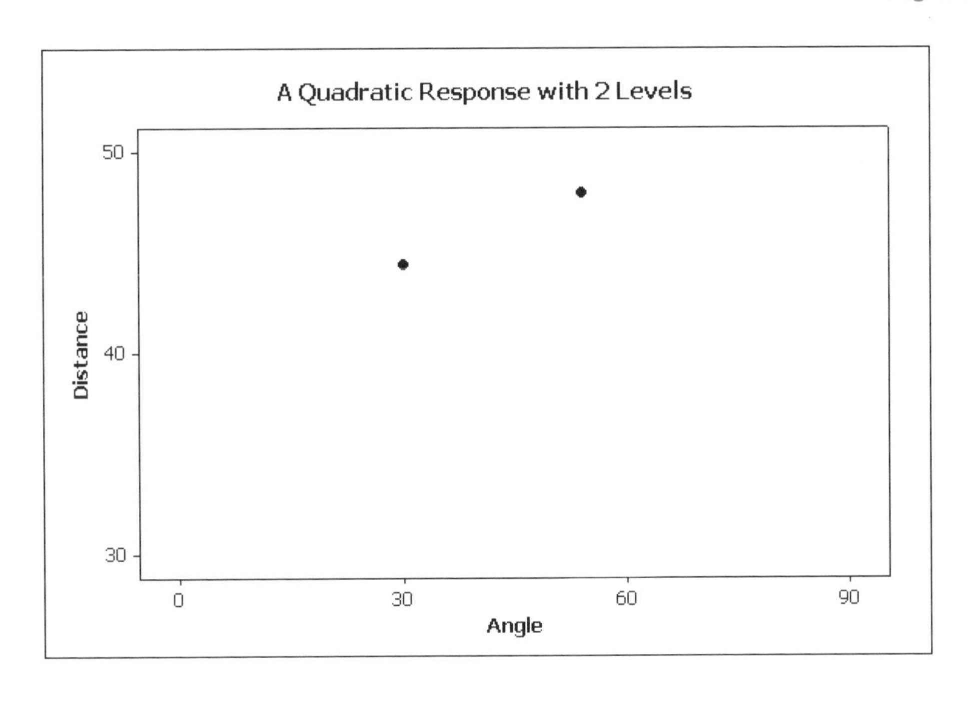

This problem can be overcome by including a **centre point** in the design. A centre point is an experimental run at which all factors are set halfway between high and low. Irrespective of the number of factors, one centre point will provide a **p**-value for curvature and put our minds at rest about the short cut we have taken.

Fig 6.4

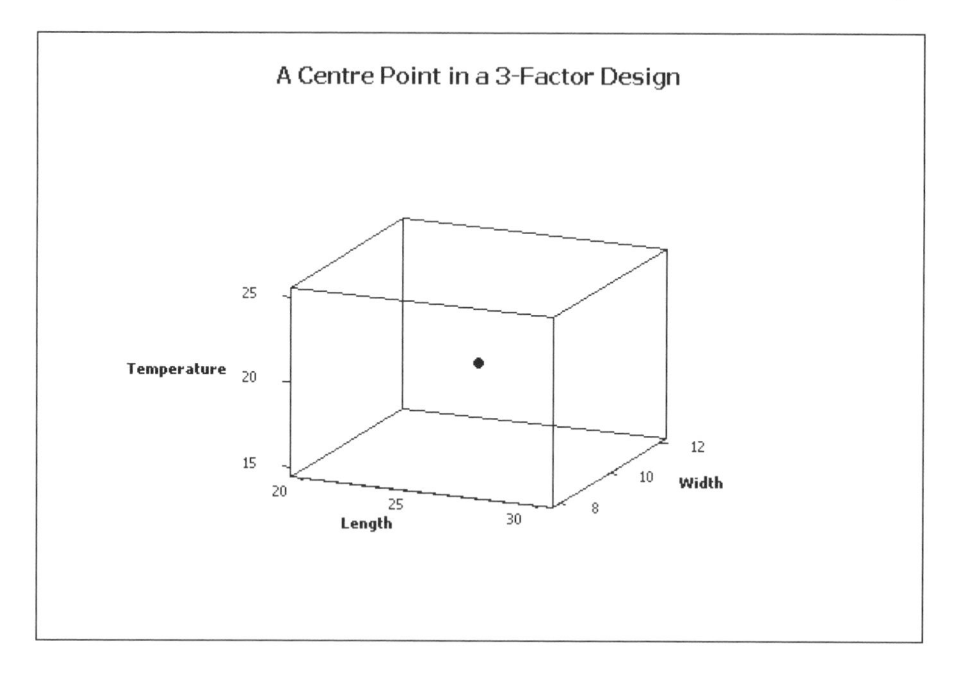

According to the curvature null hypothesis there is no curvature in any of the factors, i.e. the average response at the centre point is equal to the average response at all the corner points. Replication at the centre point is not essential, because there is replication at the corner points. However, if some additional time or material is available in an experiment, then extra centre points will improve the error variance estimate, without unbalancing the design.

A centre point makes sense only for factors with numeric levels. The levels of some factors are text, e.g. the person who throws the paper aeroplane is either Sean or Ben, and there is no halfway house. If we require a centre point in an experiment that includes such factors, we have no option but to duplicate the centre point at each of the two text levels.

Strategy 2: Fractional Factorial Designs

Even with every factor restricted to two levels, an experiment may be still too large. A second strategy to reduce the size of an experiment is to perform only a fraction of the experimental runs, e.g. 1/2 or 1/4, etc. In so doing, we deliberately exclude information about certain factor-level combinations. For example, the **fractional factorial design** illustrated below could be used to investigate the effect of three factors (length, width and air temperature) on the distance travelled by a paper aeroplane. This is a 1/2 fraction: only 4 of the 8 available design points are investigated.

Fig 6.5

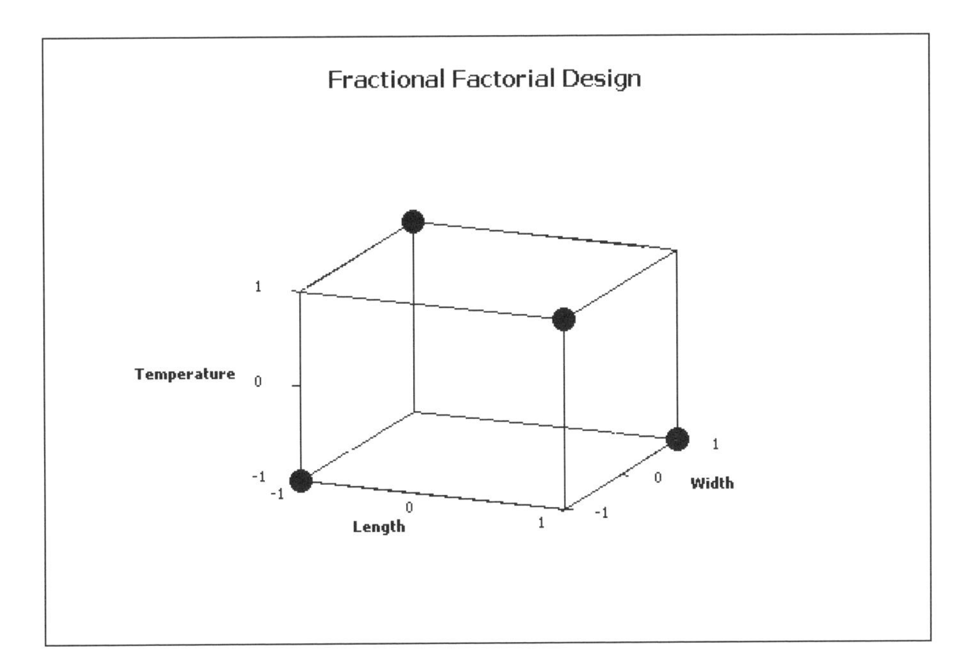

Notice that the design is balanced: of the four factor-level combinations included, two are long and two are short, etc. Of the two that are long: one is wide and one is narrow; and one is hot and one is cold.

However, fractional factorial designs can give rise to two problems. Firstly, information about certain interactions will be completely missing. If a three-factor interaction occurs at one of the missing combinations (e.g. long-wide-hot), we will simply not find out about it. Now, if we have a good knowledge of the process, we may be able to assert that these interactions would be zero anyway.

The second problem with fractional factorial designs is that information about different effects can become mixed up. This is called **confounding** or **aliasing**. Suppose that a paper aeroplane needs to be well proportioned, i.e. it should be long and wide, or else short and narrow, in order to achieve a long distance. This means that there is a length–width interaction. Look at each of the design points in the diagram above and identify which combinations give rise to large values of distance. Do you notice something? There are two favourable combinations, and two that are unfavourable. But it appears that temperature is the explanatory factor! The main effect of temperature has been confounded with the length–width interaction. Some confounding, especially of higher-order interactions, is inevitable in fractional factorial designs. However, a list of the effects that are confounded with each other (called the **alias structure**) can be identified in advance, so that we can be careful in our interpretations.

Fractional factorial designs are phenomenally powerful and popular. They answer many questions in return for a small amount of data collection.

Strategy 3: Designs without Replication

In a multi-factor experiment, a plot of the effects shows which factors stand out as important. This is especially clear if there are only a few significant effects among many – the **sparsity** principle. We can eliminate replication in an experimental design, and use an effects plot to identify significant effects. This is a fairly drastic step to take, but it does offer a third strategy for reducing the size of an experiment.

Fig 6.6

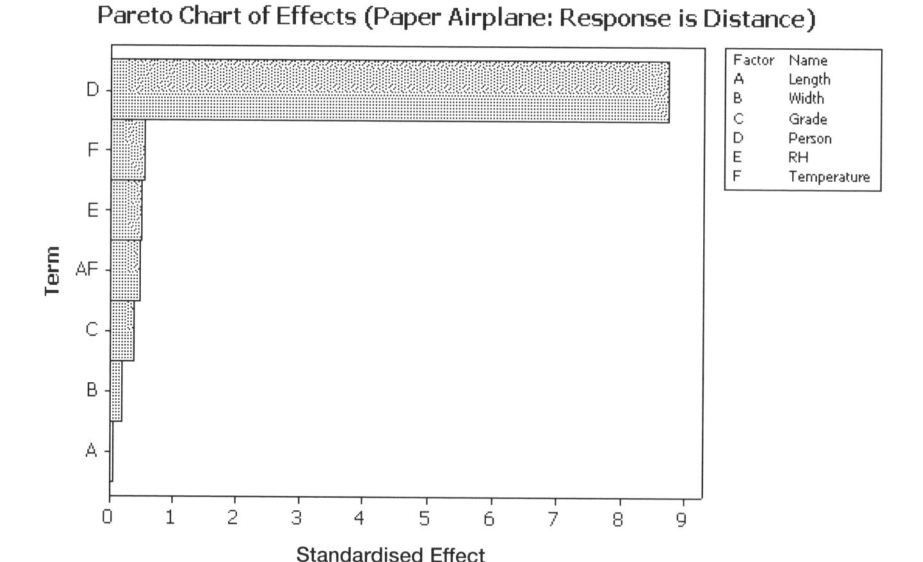

Nested Designs

In certain situations, although two factors are included in an experiment, the factors cannot be cross-classified because of the nature of the case. For example, suppose we are interested to know whether the length of beech leaves varies from tree to tree, and also from branch to branch within each tree. We may include five trees in our study, and four branches on each tree. The branches could be numbered 1, 2, 3, and 4, on each tree. But branch number 1 on tree number 1 has nothing in common with branch number 1 on tree number 2. This is because the branches are numbered within each tree, so to speak. We say that the factor 'branch' is nested within the factor 'tree', and such a design is said to be a **nested design** or **hierarchic design**.

Table 6.18

Analysis of Variance for Length

Source	DF	SS	MS	F	P
Tree	4	0.1740	0.0435	0.299	0.874
Branch	15	2.1788	0.1453	2.296	0.042
Error	20	1.2650	0.0632		
Total	39	3.6178			

The **p**-value for 'branch' is 0.042, indicating that there are significant differences between branches. The **p**-value for 'tree' is 0.874, indicating that there are no significant differences between trees that are not explained by the differences between branches: note that the **F**-value for 'tree' is obtained by dividing by the mean-square for branch, not by the mean-square for error. There is no possibility of interaction in a nested experiment.

Fixed and Random Factors

We say that a factor is fixed when all possible levels of the factor are included in an experiment. For example, an experiment considers the effect of hand and person on writing speed. Hand is a **fixed factor**, because all the levels of that factor (left and right) are included in the experiment. When we analyse the data, we would like to pick the winner – is the right or left hand faster? The **p**-value is of particular interest in such cases.

However, we cannot include every person in the experiment. We say that person is a **random factor**, because only a random sample of persons is included in the experiment. When we analyse the data, we are not interested in picking the winner from among the persons included. We are less interested in the **p**-value than in the **variance component** due to that factor, i.e. how much variation in writing speed exists among different persons, as evidenced by the random sample of persons in our experiment.

The distinction between fixed and random factors is quite similar to the distinction between descriptive and inferential statistics. The question is: Are we interested only in the factor levels before us, or are these merely a sample from a larger population of factor levels? Common random factors in business and industry are: operator, batch, and day.

After the Experiment

As with any hypothesis test, a power value of 80% is suggested for research, and 95% for validation, when applying ANOVA to experimental data. If the sample size was not decided upon before conducting the experiment, and if an important null hypothesis is accepted, it is advisable to check the power value afterwards.

Off-line experiments, performed under special conditions, do not always give a reliable indication of how a process will behave under more usual conditions. For this reason, **confirmatory runs** are strongly advised, before announcing or implementing the improvements suggested by your experimental conclusions.

It may be necessary to put a system in place in order to implement and maintain the improvements that were identified in an experiment. **Mistake-proof devices** (e.g. a high barrier that excludes SUVs) and **audits** (e.g. unannounced checks that Jessy is taking the free kicks) are two such strategies.

Having completed this chapter you should be able to:

- list some factors that might affect a response in a process with which you are familiar;
- design an experiment to investigate whether the factors affect the response;
- carry out the experiment, analyse the data, and identify improvement actions.

Problems 6.3

1. (Exercise) Working with a colleague, conduct a fractional factorial experiment to test the effect on writing speed of the six factors: Person (Ben or Doug – use your own names here), Instrument (Pencil or Pen), Case (Lower or Upper), Letter (A or F), Orientation (Horizontal or Vertical) and Hand (Left or Right). Allow eight runs (i.e. fraction = 1/8) with 2 replicates. Perform the experiment. Analyse the results. You can use the form opposite if software is not immediately available.

2. (Project) Design a fractional factorial experiment with at least four factors, in any application area of your choice. Carry out the experiment, analyse the results, and write a report under the following headings.
   (a) State the purpose of your experiment, and list the factors and factor levels.
   (b) Display the data.
   (c) Show the ANOVA table and any other relevant output.
   (d) Show an effects plot.
   (e) Express the experimental findings in simple language.

Table 6.19

Person	Instrument	Case	Letter	Orientation	Hand	Speed
Ben	Pencil	Lower	f	Vertical	Right	
Doug	Pencil	Lower	a	Horizontal	Right	
Ben	Pen	Lower	a	Vertical	Left	
Doug	Pen	Lower	f	Horizontal	Left	
Ben	Pencil	Upper	f	Horizontal	Left	
Doug	Pencil	Upper	a	Vertical	Left	
Ben	Pen	Upper	a	Horizontal	Right	
Doug	Pen	Upper	f	Vertical	Right	
Ben	Pencil	Lower	f	Vertical	Right	
Doug	Pencil	Lower	a	Horizontal	Right	
Ben	Pen	Lower	a	Vertical	Left	
Doug	Pen	Lower	f	Horizontal	Left	
Ben	Pencil	Upper	f	Horizontal	Left	
Doug	Pencil	Upper	a	Vertical	Left	
Ben	Pen	Upper	a	Horizontal	Right	
Doug	Pen	Upper	f	Vertical	Right	

7

PREDICTION

At the end of this chapter you will be able to:

- identify variables that are useful as predictors;
- make estimates using regression models;
- predict future values in time series.

Correlation and Regression

Correlation

Correlation analysis investigates the relationship between variables. If two variables are related, we can estimate the value of one variable (the **response**) by using the value of the other variable (the **predictor**). For example, if people with longer feet tend to be taller, then we can estimate someone's height from the length of their footprint. This approach is useful when the response is difficult to measure directly, or when its value is unavailable, or when it cannot be known until some time in the future.

Example: The shoe-sizes and heights of eight people are shown below.

Table 7.1

Shoe-Size	Height in cm
6	175
3	157
6	165
5	165
4	163
7	178
7	170
4	167

The first step in analysing the relationship between two variables is to draw a **scatterplot**.

Fig 7.1

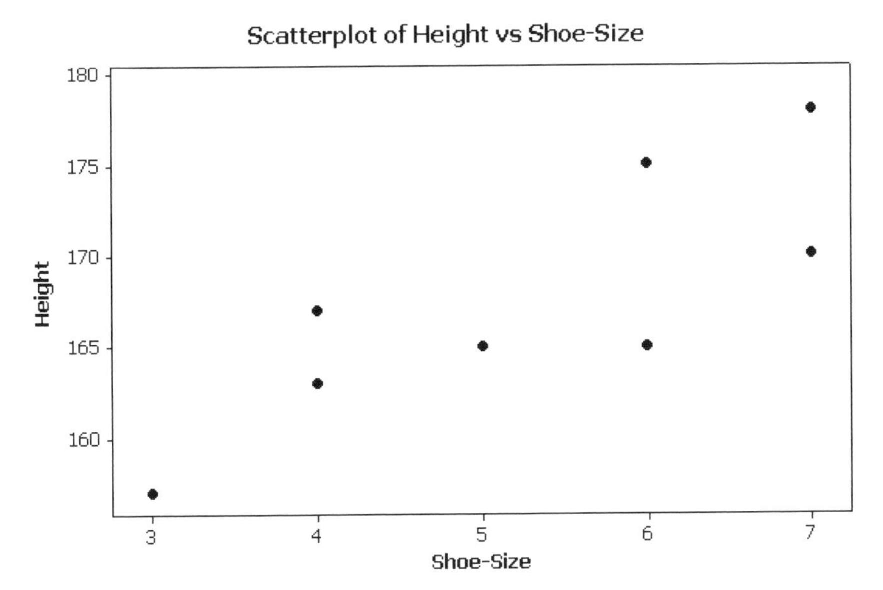

We can see that as shoe-size increases, height tends to increase also, i.e. there is some **positive correlation** between shoe-size and height. The correlation is fairly strong: although a line could be drawn through the points, the points do not lie close to such a line.

Example: The ages and prices of a number of small cars were as follows.

Table 7.2

Age	Price
4	8250
5	6995
0	14795
1	12750
2	11750
3	9950
9	2500
8	3750
7	4900
6	5950

A scatterplot of these data is shown.

Fig 7.2

There is **negative correlation** i.e. as age increases, price tends to decrease. On this occasion the correlation is strong: the points exhibit a high degree of linearity.

Of course, some variables are not correlated at all, either positively or negatively. A scatter diagram will reveal a **plum-pudding model**, with the points randomly scattered, like the currants in a plum pudding.

Fig 7.3

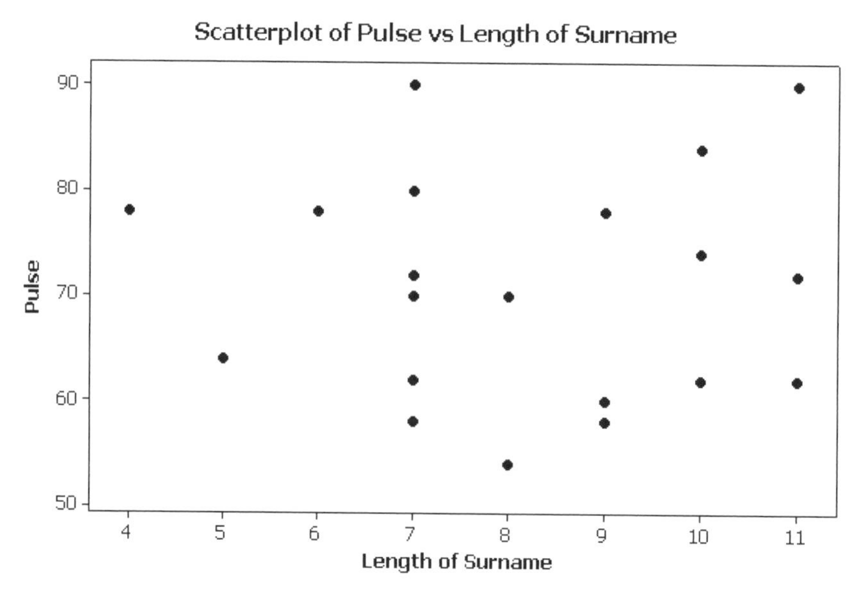

Correlation does not prove causation. When correlation between two variables is revealed by an observational study, this does not prove that **X** causes **Y**. It simply means that the value of **X** is useful when predicting the value of **Y**. We can predict the value of **Y** more precisely if the value of **X** is known. To prove causation requires a designed experiment in which the values of **X** can be randomly assigned.

The Correlation Coefficient

The **correlation coefficient** (**r**) is a statistic that measures the degree of linearity between two variables. Its value always lies between −1 and 1. The sign of **r** (+ or −) indicates the type of correlation (positive or negative). The size of **r** indicates the strength of the correlation: values close to zero indicate that the correlation is weak.

A formula for **r** is provided, but it makes more sense to let your calculator or software calculate it for you.

Formula 7.1

Correlation Coefficient

$$r = \frac{n\sum XY - \sum X \sum Y}{\sqrt{\{n\sum X^2 - (\sum X)^2\} \times \{n\sum Y^2 - (\sum Y)^2\}}}$$

Example: To calculate **r** for the shoe-size and height data, first compute these statistics.

$n = 8$
$\Sigma X = 42$
$\Sigma X^2 = 236$
$\Sigma Y = 1340$
$\Sigma Y^2 = 224766$
$\Sigma XY = 7092$

Now, substitute these values into the formula for **r**.

$r = (8 \times 7092 - 42 \times 1340) / \sqrt{\{(8 \times 236 - 42^2) \times (8 \times 224766 - 1340^2)\}}$

$r = 456 / \sqrt{\{124 \times 2528\}}$

$r = 0.8145$, i.e. fairly strong, positive correlation.

In the case of the age and price data, $r = -0.9956$, i.e. very strong, negative correlation.

Coefficient of Determination

The square of the correlation coefficient, r^2, is called the **coefficient of determination**. It is usually expressed as a percentage, and it indicates the proportion of the variation in **Y** which is **explained** by the variation in **X**. For example, for the 'age and price' data, $r^2 = 99.1\%$. This tells us that the reason why the cars have different prices is largely to do with age. The residual variation, $1 - r^2 = 0.9\%$, is **unexplained variation**. This is the proportion of the variation in price that cannot be explained by a linear relationship with age, because some cars of the same age have different prices.

The proportion of unexplained variation in the population tends to be slightly greater than in the sample, by an amount **(n − 1)/(n − 2)**. This is the ratio of the degrees of freedom before and after introducing a linear relationship. There are only **n − 2** degrees of freedom for error when a simple linear relationship is introduced, because any two points will lie on a line, with no error. The population coefficient of determination can be estimated by calculating **r² (adjusted)**.

Formula 7.2

r² adjusted

$$r^2\,(adj) = 1-(1-r^2)\frac{(n-1)}{(n-p-1)}$$

p is the number of predictor variables.

For the 'age and price' data, **r²** (adjusted) = 99.0%. This indicates that 99% of the variation in price of **all** such cars is explained by the variation in age. If we restrict ourselves to cars that are all the same age, the variance in price will be reduced by about 99% of its current value.

In the case of the shoe-size and height data, **r²** (adjusted) = 60.7%. Can you say what this signifies?

Regression Equation

Having established that a linear relationship exists between two variables, the next step is to identify the line that describes the relationship.

Fig 7.4

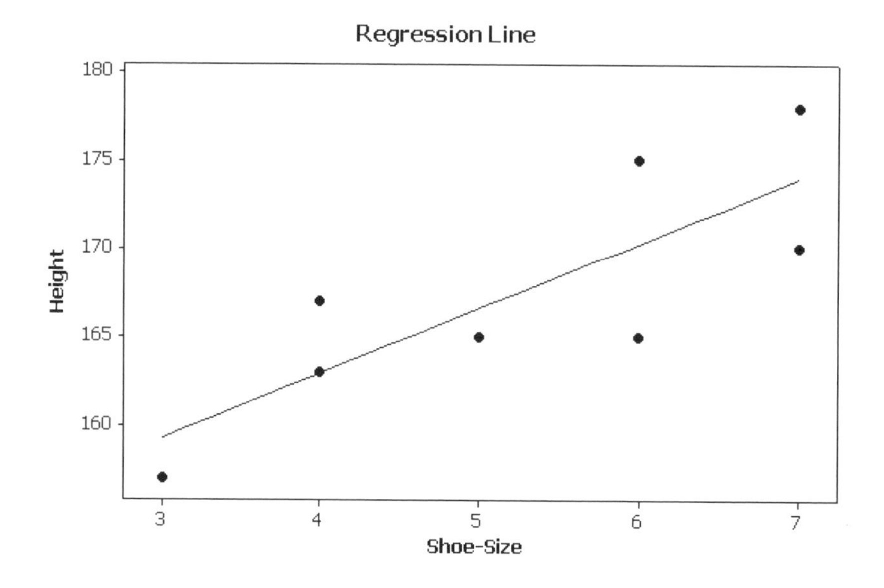

The equation of a line has the form: **Y = a + bX**, where

'**b**' is the slope of the line, i.e. the increase in **Y** which is associated with an increase of one unit in **X**, and '**a**' is the intercept on the **Y**-axis, i.e. the value of **Y** when **X** is zero.

Fig 7.5

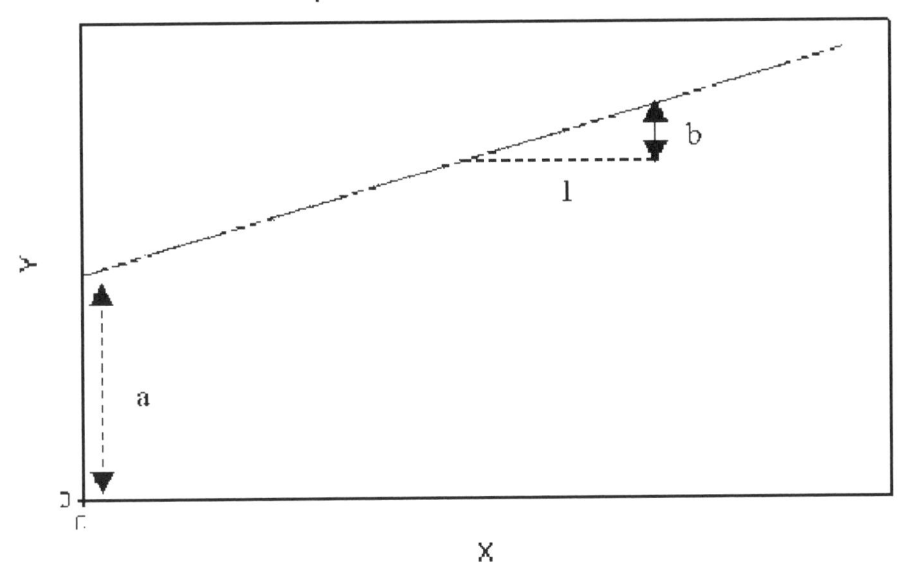

In a regression equation, **b** is called the **regression coefficient**, and **a** is called the **regression constant**. The regression line shown above is described by the equation:
Height = 148.2 + 3.7 Shoe-Size

The regression coefficient indicates that every one unit increase in shoe-size tends to be associated with an increase of 3.7 cm in height. The regression constant indicates that people who wear a size zero shoe (if such a thing existed) would be 148.2 cm tall, on average. Notice that the regression constant does not always make sense in isolation (because zero may not be a realistic value for **X**), but it is always meaningful as part of the regression equation.

The regression equation for the age and price data is:
Price = 14191 − 1340 Age
Can you explain what these numbers signify?
The following equations can be used to calculate **a** and **b** by hand, if required.

Formula 7.3

Regression Equation

$$Y = a + bX$$

$$b = \frac{n\sum XY - \sum X \sum Y}{n\sum X^2 - (\sum X)^2}$$

$$a = \frac{\sum Y - b\sum X}{n}$$

Example: To calculate **a** and **b** for the shoe-size and height data, first compute these statistics.

$n = 8$
$\Sigma X = 42$
$\Sigma X^2 = 236$
$\Sigma Y = 1340$
$\Sigma XY = 7092$

Next, substitute these values into the formula for **b**.

$b = (8 \times 7092 - 42 \times 1340) / (8 \times 236 - 42^2)$
$b = 456 / 124$
$b = 3.677$

Now, substitute into the formula for **a**.

$a = (1340 - 3.677 \times 42) / 8$
$a = 148.2$
The regression equation is: $Y = 148.2 + 3.7X$

Making Predictions

The regression equation can be used to predict new values of **Y** (height), by substituting any value of **X** (shoe-size) into the equation:

e.g. If $X = 6.5$, $Y = 148.2 + 3.7X = 172.25$
e.g. If $X = 14$, $Y = 148.2 + 3.7X = 200$

Notice that the first prediction used a value of **X** that lies inside the range of the sample data. This type of prediction is called **interpolation**, and it is quite reliable. The second prediction used a value of **X** that lies outside the range of the sample data. This type of prediction is called **extrapolation**. Extrapolation can lead to predictions that have very large errors, as a result of **non-linearity** or **discontinuity** in the relationship between **X** and **Y**, as illustrated below.

Fig 7.6

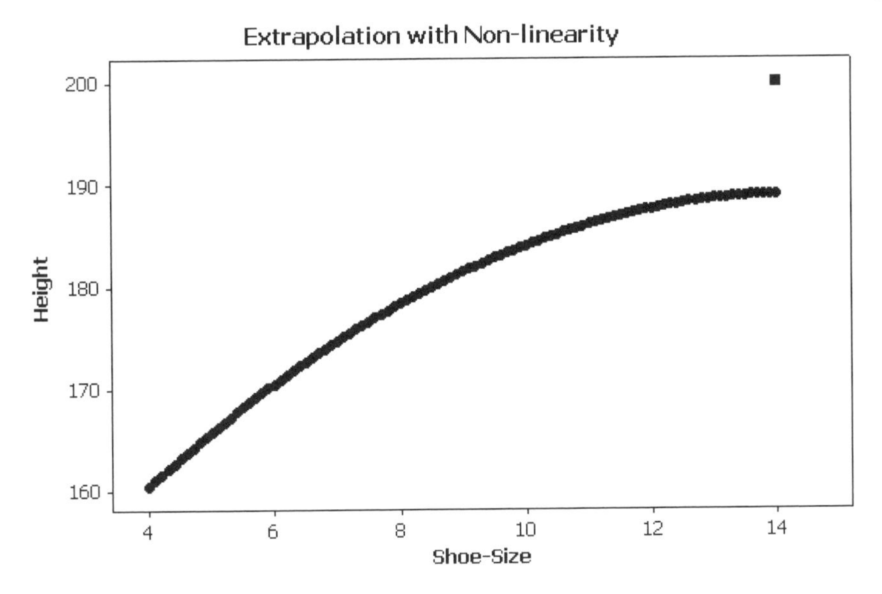

In the first case, the predicted value is very much in error, because the underlying relationship between height and shoe-size is described by a curve rather than a straight line, but this is not noticed over the limited range of the sample data.

Fig 7.7

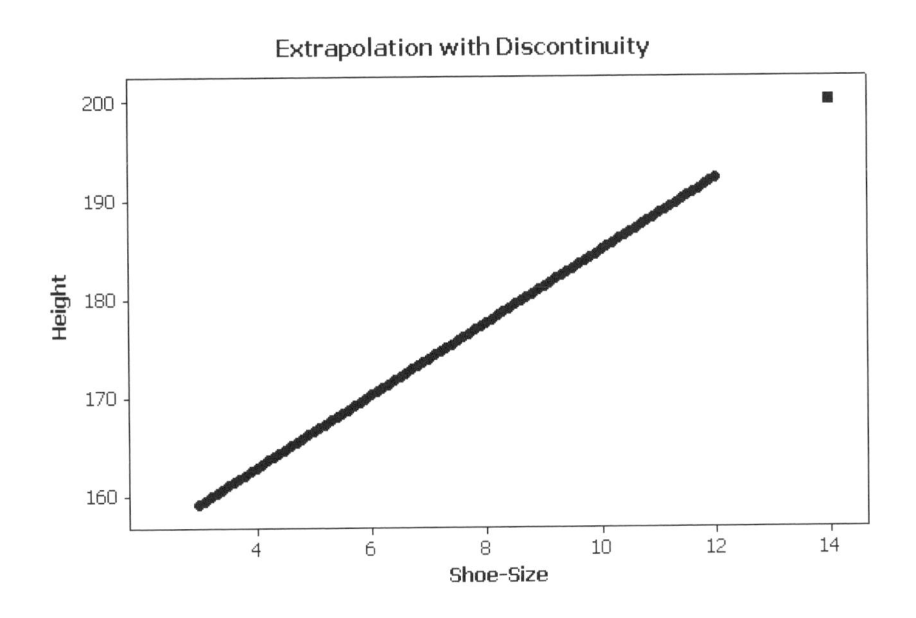

In the second case, the predicted value is correct in theory, but meaningless in practice, because this manufacturer does not produce any shoes larger than size 12.

The Regression Model

A regression equation predicts **Y** values, but these predictions are not perfect. For one thing, '**a**' and '**b**' are sample statistics, that merely estimate the population parameters α and β. Also, while the regression line describes the behaviour of the average **Y**, the individual values of **Y** lie above and below the line. Therefore the complete **model** for **Y** is as follows.

Model 7.1

Simple Regression Model

$$Y = \alpha + \beta X + \epsilon$$

The line of **best fit** is the line that achieves the smallest errors (ϵ) in predicting the **Y** values. Graphically, the errors are the vertical distances from the points to the line, since the vertical distances represent the errors in **Y**. These errors are illustrated by the short vertical line segments on the graph below. The regression line is chosen so that the sum of squared errors is a minimum and therefore it is called the **least squares** line.

Fig 7.8

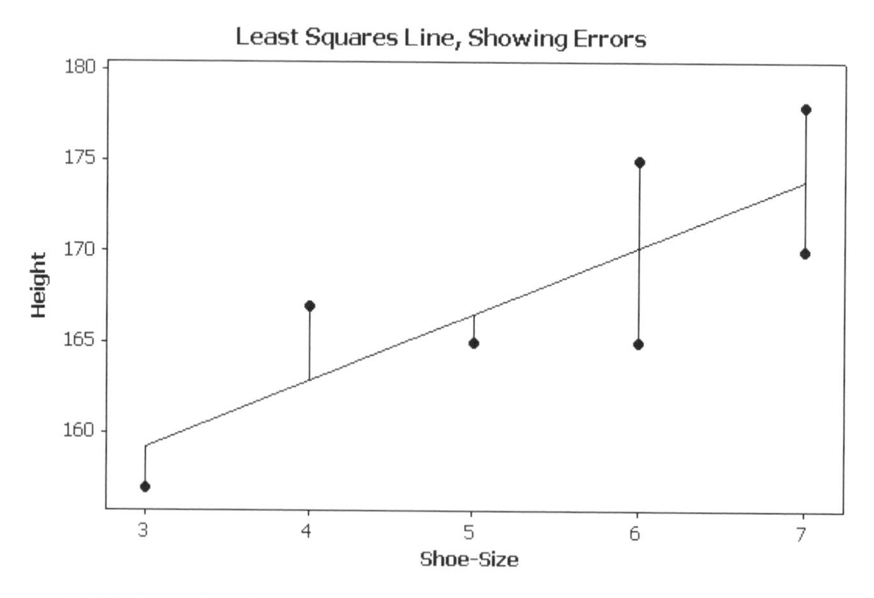

From this it follows that the least squares regression equation of **Y** on **X** is not the same, in general, as the least squares regression equation of **X** on **Y**. So if we want to predict shoe-size from height, we need to calculate a new regression equation, with height as **X** and shoe-size as **Y**.

It is usually assumed that the errors (also called residuals) are normally distributed with a constant variance that does not depend on **X**. This means that for a fixed value of **X**, the population of **Y** is normal, with mean $\alpha + \beta$**X**, and standard deviation σ. Every **Y** value in the sample is assumed to have been drawn at random from such a population, therefore the values of **Y** must not be selected in advance, although the **X** values can be preselected if desired. In a situation where the experimenter has selected the **X** values, and needs to predict **X** from **Y**, the regression equation of **Y** on **X** should first be constructed and then transformed to provide a formula for **X**.

The assumptions can be tested by **residual analysis**. A histogram of the residuals should look approximately normal, and a plot of residuals versus fits should show the points forming a horizontal belt of roughly uniform width.

Hypothesis Testing in Regression

The most important hypothesis in regression is:

H_0: $\beta = 0$

This null hypothesis states that **X** is not a useful predictor of **Y**. If this null hypothesis is accepted, it indicates that there is no predictive relationship at all between **X** and **Y**, and the analysis is over. Graphically, this null hypothesis states that the population regression line is horizontal.

Fig 7.9

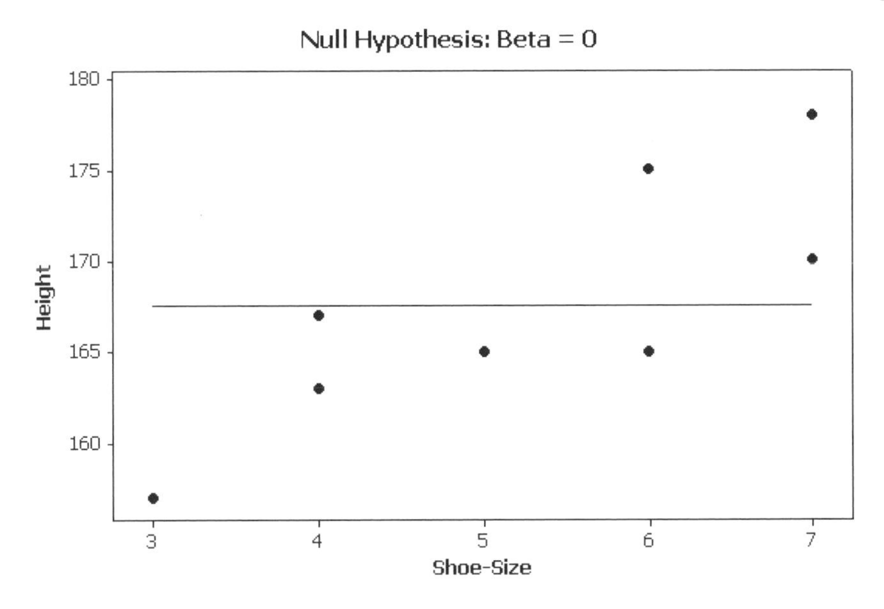

A second hypothesis may also be of interest.

H_0: $\alpha = 0$

If this null hypothesis is accepted, it means that the population regression line may pass through the origin. This means that **Y** is directly proportional to **X**: any change in **X** is matched by an identical percentage change in **Y**. If zero is a meaningful value for **X**, it also means that the corresponding average value of **Y** is zero.

Fig 7.10

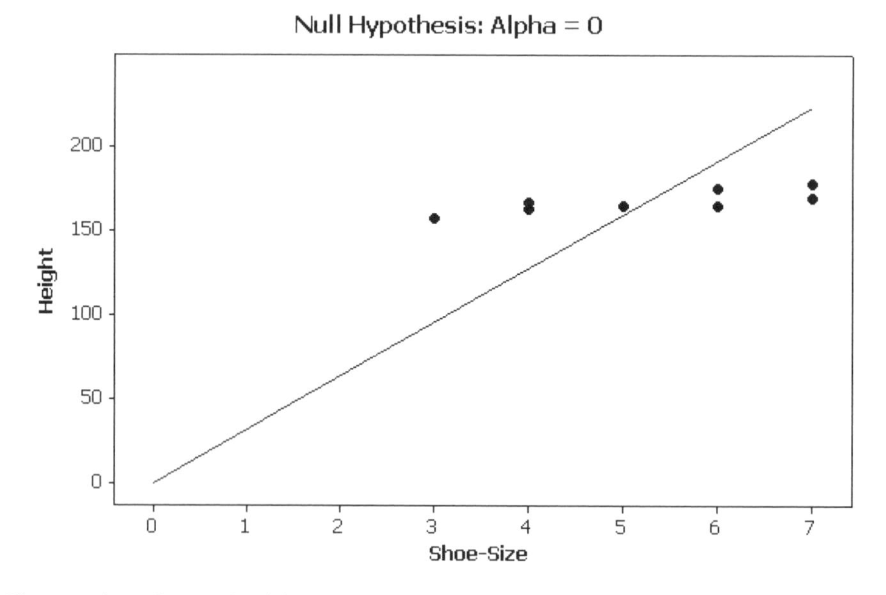

The **p**-values for each of these hypotheses are shown below, in relation to the shoe-size and height data.

Table 7.3

Predictor	Coef	SE Coef	T	P
Constant	148.194	5.809	25.51	0.000
Shoe-Size	3.677	1.070	3.44	0.014

The **p**-value for shoe-size is 0.014, which is less than 5%, so we reject the hypothesis that the population regression line is horizontal. We conclude that shoe-size is a useful predictor of height.

The **p**-value for the constant is 0.000, which is less than 5%, so we reject the hypothesis that the regression line passes through the origin. We conclude that height is not directly proportional to shoe-size, e.g. people who wear a size 8 shoe are not twice as tall as people who wear a size 4 shoe.

Confidence Intervals in Regression

The following output predicts the height corresponding to a shoe-size of 6.5.

Table 7.4

Fit	SE Fit	95% CI	95% PI
172.10	2.00	(167.20, 176.99)	(160.69, 183.50)

The fit (i.e. fitted value) is a point estimate: we expect a person who wears a size 6.5 shoe to be 172.1 cm tall. The 95% CI is a confidence interval for the **average** height of all people who wear size 6.5 shoes. The prediction interval (PI) is a 95% confidence interval for the height of an **individual** person who wears a size 6.5 shoe. The CI estimates $\alpha + \beta\mathbf{X}$ with 95% confidence, i.e. the height of the population regression line when $\mathbf{X} = 6.5$. The PI estimates $\alpha + \beta\mathbf{X} + \epsilon$ with 95% confidence, i.e. the height of an individual point on the graph when $\mathbf{X} = 6.5$. The prediction interval, in particular, is sensitive to the normality assumption. Also, while a single confidence or prediction interval can be quoted with 95% confidence, multiple intervals that are based on the same set of data should be used cautiously, as they do not have an independent probability of 95% of being correct.

Problems 7.1

1. It may be possible to predict the length of grass, in cm, using the number of days since mowing.

Table 7.5

Days	Length
2	3.2
4	3.9
6	4.5
8	4.8
10	5.5

(a) Calculate $\mathbf{r}^2$ (adjusted) and explain what it signifies.
(b) Draw a scatterplot and find the regression equation.
(c) Test the two hypotheses $\beta = 0$ and $\alpha = 0$.
(d) Predict the length of the grass after 20 days.

2. It may be possible to predict the juice content of an orange, in ml, using the weight of the orange, in grams.

Table 7.6

Weight	Juice
180	105
215	135
250	140
425	225

(a) Calculate r^2 (adjusted) and explain what it signifies.
(b) Draw a scatterplot and find the regression equation.
(c) Test the two hypotheses $\beta = 0$ and $\alpha = 0$.
(d) Predict the juice content of an orange that weights 290 g.

3. It may be possible to predict the daily food intake of a dog, in grams, using the weight of the dog, in kg.

Table 7.7

Weight	Food
8	157
11	142
12	138
15	183
20	204
28	309
32	333

(a) Calculate r^2 (adjusted) and explain what it signifies.
(b) Draw a scatterplot and find the regression equation.
(c) Test the two hypotheses $\beta = 0$ and $\alpha = 0$.
(d) Predict the daily food intake of another dog that weighs 15 kg.

4. (Project) Use regression analysis to investigate the relationship between some predictor and some response, in any application area of your choice. Collect at least 10 data pairs and write a report under the following headings.
(a) State the purpose of your investigation, and explain how you applied randomisation to the data collection.
(b) Display the data, a scatter plot, and the regression equation.

(c) Explain what r^2 (adjusted) means in this situation.

(d) Test the two hypotheses $\beta = 0$ and $\alpha = 0$, and explain what your conclusions mean.

(e) Construct a prediction interval for the value of the response corresponding to some value of the predictor variable, and explain what your answer means.

Time Series and Index Numbers

Time Series

A **time series** is a set of data which represents the change in a variable over time. The variable could be sales, traffic volume, rainfall, etc. Time-series analysis seeks to find patterns in the data, by breaking down (**decomposing**) the time series into **components**. This can lead to **forecasts** that are used to support planning and decision making. The typical components of a time series are the following.

(a) **Random Variation**: Time-series data are affected by a multitude of small, unpredictable events, which can cause the figures to rise or fall slightly. Therefore it is virtually impossible to make perfect forecasts. However the magnitude of the random component can be measured, using the standard deviation, and this can be used to construct confidence limits for predictions.

(b) **Trend**: This describes whether the figures are moving upward, moving downward, or remaining stationary, over time. A regression equation of the data (**Y**) on time (**t**) can be used to model the trend.

Model 7.2

Time Series with Trend Only

$$Y = \alpha + \beta t + \epsilon$$

Example: The profits of a theme park (in €m) during its first six years of operation are shown. Predict the profits in year seven.

Table 7.8

Time	Profits
1	3
2	11
3	17
4	22
5	27
6	32

Working by hand or with software, we obtain the regression equation:

Profits = −1.13 + 5.66 Time

This shows the magnitude of the trend: profits are rising at an average rate of 5.66 per year.

Substituting **t** = 7 we obtain our forecast:

Profits = 38.5

Predictions always involve extrapolation: predictions for the near future can be quite reliable – those for the distant future are less so.

(c) **Seasonal Variation**: This describes regular up-and-down movements in the figures, which are repeated at yearly intervals or more frequently. The seasonal component (**C_s**) has a different value for each season, representing the amount (+ or −) by which the average increases at that season.

Model 7.3

Time Series with Trend and Seasonal Variation

$$Y = \alpha + \beta t + C_S + \epsilon$$

Example: The number of hotel rooms booked in each quarter (i.e. season) of a three-year period is shown below, in hundreds. Predict the number of bookings for the next quarter.

Table 7.9

Year	Quarter	Time	Data
1	1	1	14
1	2	2	33
1	3	3	44
1	4	4	25
2	1	5	28
2	2	6	43
2	3	7	53
2	4	8	26
3	1	9	38
3	2	10	47
3	3	11	63
3	4	12	39

We begin by calculating the trend using the regression equation of data on time. In this context, time is always a simple variable that counts the number of data that have arisen.

Data = 23.3 + 2.22 Time

Substituting **t** = 13 we obtain our **initial** forecast for the next quarter:

Initial forecast = 52.18

We have not yet taken seasonal variation into account. Now, using the regression equation, we calculate the trend figure for each time period in the data set, and also the residuals (i.e. data minus trend).

Fig 7.11

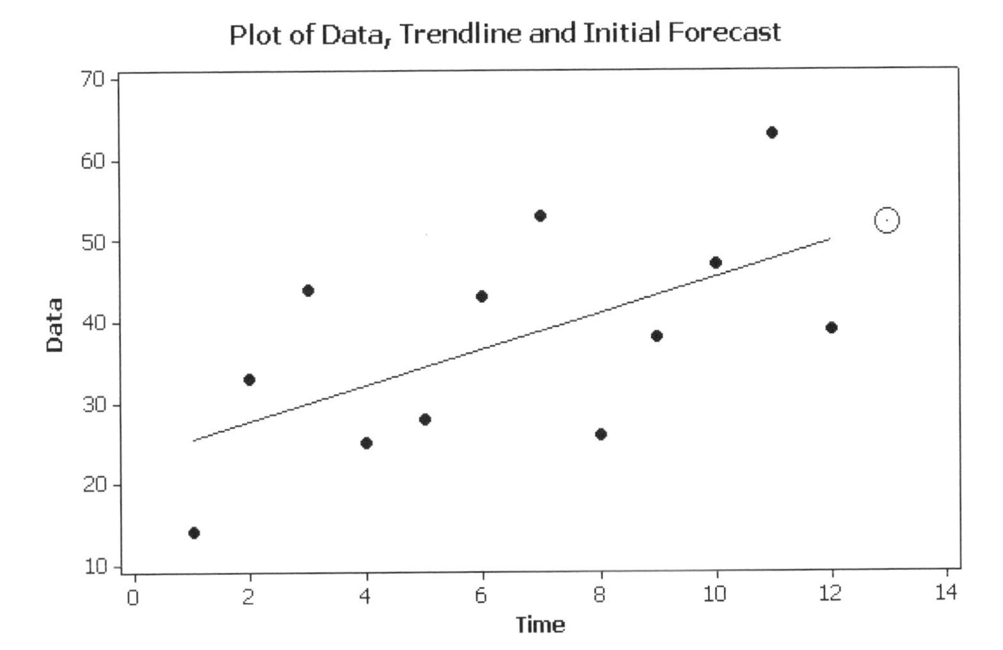

Table 7.10

Year	Quarter	Time	Data	Trend	Residual
1	1	1	14	25.54	−11.54
1	2	2	33	27.76	5.24
1	3	3	44	29.98	14.02
1	4	4	25	32.20	−7.20
2	1	5	28	34.42	−6.42
2	2	6	43	36.64	6.36
2	3	7	53	38.86	14.14
2	4	8	26	41.08	−15.08
3	1	9	38	43.30	-5.30
3	2	10	47	45.52	1.48
3	3	11	63	47.74	15.26
3	4	12	39	49.96	−10.96

These residuals include a seasonal component: it is easy to see that quarters 1 and 4 tend to be low, while quarters 2 and 3 tend to be high. The seasonal component can be estimated by calculating the average residual for each season.

$C_1 = (-11.54 - 6.42 - 5.30)/3 = -7.75$

$C_2 = (5.24 + 6.36 + 1.48)/3 = 4.36$

$C_3 = (14.02 + 14.14 + 15.26)/3 = 14.47$

$C_4 = (-7.20 - 15.08 - 10.96)/3 = -11.08$

Our forecast relates to quarter 1, so we must add the relevant seasonal component to our initial forecast.

Final forecast = $52.18 + (-7.75) = 44.43$

The seasonal components can also be used to clarify the underlying behaviour of a series. As new figures arise in the data series they can be **seasonally adjusted** by subtracting the relevant seasonal component. For example, room bookings are almost certain to rise in the second quarter of the year, but this does not signify an underlying growth in the business, unless the seasonally adjusted figure is also up.

The hotel data can be analysed by software using a **general linear model**, by specifying 'time' as a **covariate**, and 'quarter' as a term in the model.

(d) **Cyclical Variation**: This describes slow, up-and-down movements in the figures, which occur in cycles that are longer than one year. These movements represent long-term changes in the trend. To identify the cyclical component in a time series we need data extending over a very long period. Even with this, it is difficult to identify a pattern for cyclical variation, and even more difficult to project this forward to make a forecast. It is common to simply ignore cyclical variation for short-term predictions.

(e) **Sudden Shifts**: It is wise to remember that the most careful forecast can be shattered by an unexpected event such as a political crisis, a natural disaster or the sudden emergence of an economic rival. Earlier data rarely provide any clues about the approach of such events, but a wide knowledge of the context may give some warning.

Index Numbers

Often the variable in a time series is complex, e.g. the 'cost of living'. Such a variable can be represented by an **index number** such as the **consumer price index** (CPI). Basically, an index is any number, expressed as a percentage of another number. The other number is called the **base**. We begin with a simple example.

Example: The output of blackberries from a fruit farm was 11 tonnes in year 1, 13 tonnes in year 2 and 14 tonnes in year 3. We wish to represent this information as an index-number series, with year 1 as the base year.

Year 1: 100

Year 2: 13/11 × 100 = 118

Year 3: 14/11 × 100 = 127

Formula 7.4

Index Numbers

$$Index = \frac{Y_n}{Y_o} \times 100$$

n is the current period   **0** is the base period

Price Indices

Often we need to consider the prices of a 'basket' of commodities, rather than just one. An **aggregate index** can be used to deal with a collection of variables.

Example: In year 1, a potato-crisp manufacturer used the following recipe: 53 g of potato, 5 g of oil and 2 g of salt. The prices of some of these ingredients, especially oil, rose at the beginning of year 2. We wish to express the increase in the price of all the ingredients as an index number, taking year 1 as the base year. Quantities are denoted by **q**, and prices are denoted **p**, in cent per kilogram.

Table 7.11

	p (Year 1)	q (Year 1)	p (Year 2)
Potato	34	53	34
Oil	88	5	110
Salt	40	2	42

It would not be appropriate to add together the year 2 prices (34 + 110 + 42), and compare this figure with the sum of the year 1 prices, because such an approach does not take into account the relative importance of the different ingredients. For example, a 1-cent rise in the price of potato is more than ten times as important as a 1-cent rise in the price of oil, because the quantities of potato used are so much greater. It makes sense to construct a weighted aggregate index, using the quantities as weights. In this way, we will be comparing the cost of the 'bag' of ingredients at year 2 prices, with its cost at year 1 prices.

$(34\times53 + 110\times5 + 42\times2) / (34\times53 + 88\times5 + 40\times2) \times 100 = 104.9$

This expresses the change in all the prices very simply. We have used the following formula.

Formula 7.5

Laspeyres Price Index

$$L_p = \frac{\sum p_n q_o}{\sum p_o q_o} \times 100$$

The **Laspeyres price index** uses base-year quantities as weights.

Considering the big increase in the price of oil in year 2, the manufacturer might decide to modify the recipe so that less oil is used. The quantity of oil used per bag could be reduced by 2 g, and the quantities of potato and salt could be increased by 1 g each. This would help to reduce the effect of the oil-price increase. Of course, the recipe might be changed for other reasons too. The year 2 recipe is shown below, alongside all the original data.

Table 7.12

	p (Year 1)	q (Year 1)	p (Year 2)	q (Year 2)
Potato	34	53	34	54
Oil	88	5	110	3
Salt	40	2	42	3

There is now another way to calculate an aggregate price index. We can compare the cost of the new bag of ingredients at year 2 prices, with its cost at year 1 prices.
$(34\times54 + 110\times3 + 42\times3) / (34\times54 + 88\times3 + 40\times3) \times 100 = 103.2$

As expected, the price increase is smaller with this approach. This time we have used the following formula.

Formula 7.6

Paasche Price Index

$$P_p = \frac{\sum p_n q_n}{\sum p_o q_n} \times 100$$

The **Paasche price index** uses current-year quantities as weights. We now have two different index-number series, which both claim to represent the change in prices.

Laspeyres: 100, 104.9

Paasche: 100, 103.2

The advantage of Laspeyres is that it uses base-year quantities: since the current prices are being compared with base-year prices, it seems appropriate that the comparison should be 'based' on base-year information as much as possible. The disadvantage of Laspeyres is that, over time, the quantities used may become out of date and irrelevant, e.g. an old Laspeyres price index might include the prices of telegrams rather than text messages. Laspeyres price indices also tend to overstate price increases, because alternatives will be sought for commodities that rise substantially in price.

The advantage of Paasche is that the weights (quantities) used are up to date and relevant. The disadvantage of Paasche is that information on current quantities may not be available until the end of the current period, or even later. Paasche price indices also tend to understate price increases, because not everyone can switch over to alternative commodities, and even those who do may be less satisfied with the new experience. For example, the new crisps may have an inferior taste.

A balance between these two options is provided by the **Fisher ideal price index**, which is the **geometric mean** of the Laspeyres price index and the Paasche price index.

Formula 7.7

Fisher Ideal Index

$$Fisher = \sqrt{Laspeyres \times Paasche}$$

Fisher ideal price index = $\sqrt{(104.9 \times 103.2)} = 104.0$

Quantity Indices

In the same way that we use index numbers to measure price changes, we may wish to measure the changes in the quantities of goods purchased from year to year. It makes sense to construct a weighted index, giving greater weight to the quantities of goods that are more important. For example, an extra tonne of jewellery is more important than an extra tonne of potatoes. The prices of the various goods may be used as weights.

Example: A supplier maintains contact with an overseas customer by telephone, and by occasional visits that involve air travel. The number of flights and the number of telephone-minutes devoted to this relationship are shown below, for year 1 and year 2, together with the relevant prices. Has the quantity of contact increased?

Table 7.13

	p (Telephone)	q (Telephone)	p (Flights)	q (Flights)
Year 1	0.112	350	69	7
Year 2	0.112	600	84	4

Looking at the data, we see that the amount of telephone contact has increased, but the number of flights has reduced. Some weighting procedure must be used that measures the relative importance of a flight and a telephone-minute, and price is the obvious choice for weights. We can use either base-year prices, to give a Laspeyres quantity index, or current-year prices, to give a Paasche quantity index.

Formula 7.8

Laspeyres Quantity Index

$$L_q = \frac{\Sigma p_o q_n}{\Sigma p_o q_o} \times 100$$

The **Laspeyres quantity index** uses base-year prices as weights.
$\mathbf{L_q}$ = (0.112×600 + 69×4) / (0.112×350 + 69×7) × 100 = 65.72

Formula 7.9

Paasche Quantity Index

$$P_q = \frac{\Sigma p_n q_n}{\Sigma p_n q_o} \times 100$$

The **Paasche quantity index** uses current-year prices as weights.

$\mathbf{P_q}$ = (0.112 ×600 + 84 ×4) / (0.112 ×350 + 84 ×7) × 100 = 64.29

As before, the **Fisher ideal quantity index** is the geometric mean of the Laspeyres and Paasche indices.

Fisher ideal quantity index = √(65.72 × 64.29) = 65.0

Value Indices

Price indices address the question, 'By how much have the prices increased?' Quantity indices address the question, 'By how much have the quantities increased?' We may wish to pose a third question, namely, 'How much more money is being spent?' The change in the total expenditure on a set of goods can depend on a change in prices, or a change in quantities, or both. It can be expressed by a **value index**, which compares the cost of current-year quantities at current-year prices, with the cost of base-year quantities at base-year prices.

Formula 7.10

Value Index

$$V = \frac{\Sigma p_n q_n}{\Sigma p_o q_o} \times 100$$

The value index for the customer contact data is:

V = (0.112×600 + 84×4) / (0.112×350 + 69×7) × 100 = 77.21

Change of Base

We may wish to compare two index-number series, such as the Dow Jones and the NASDAQ share price indices.

Table 7.14

Month End	Dow Jones	NASDAQ
Jan	10489.9	2062.41
Feb	10766.2	2051.72
Mar	10503.8	1999.23
Apr	10192.5	1921.65
May	10467.5	2068.22

Which index changed more over this period? This question is difficult to answer, because the two index-number series have different bases. If we make January the base for both series, the comparison becomes easy. So we express all the Dow Jones figures as percentages of 10489.9, and all the NASDAQ figures as percentages of 2062.41.

Table 7.15

Month End	Dow Jones	NASDAQ
Jan	100.0	100.0
Feb	102.6	99.5
Mar	100.1	96.9
Apr	97.2	93.2
May	99.8	100.3

Now it can easily be seen that the rise in the NASDAQ is slightly greater than the fall in the Dow Jones.

Changing the base of an index number series also illustrates the difference between a **percentage point** increase and a per cent increase. Between January and May, the NASDAQ rose by 0.3 per cent, but in the original series this rise is seen to be 5.81 percentage points, i.e. 2068.22 minus 2062.41. These percentage points refer to the original base of the NASDAQ, way back in February 1971, when NASDAQ = 100.

Deflation of Data

The earnings of a graduate in years 1, 2, 3 and 4, in euro, were 24000, 24500, 26000 and 26500, respectively. Although these data represent a rise in earnings each year, prices also rose during the same period. The question is, 'Did the purchasing power of the graduate rise each year?' To answer this question, we compare the graduate's earnings with the consumer price index. By dividing each year's earnings by the corresponding value of the CPI, and multiplying the result by 100, we obtain the **deflated series**, which represents the value of the earnings in the base year of the CPI.

Table 7.16

Year	Earnings	CPI	Deflated Earnings
1	24000	100.0	24000
2	24500	103.4	23694
3	26000	106.6	24390
4	26500	110.0	24091

We see, for example, that real earnings in year 4 are lower than in year 3, and have the equivalent purchasing power of 24091 in year 1, the base year of the CPI.

PROBLEMS 7.2

1. Department-store revenue for each quarter of a three-year period is shown below in thousands of euro. Predict the revenue for the next quarter.

Table 7.17

Year	Quarter	Time	Revenue
1	1	1	71
1	2	2	80
1	3	3	53
1	4	4	48
2	1	5	69
2	2	6	70
2	3	7	46
2	4	8	43
3	1	9	60
3	2	10	66
3	3	11	36
3	4	12	34

2. The profits of a garden centre for each quarter of a three-year period are shown below in thousands of euro. Predict the profit for the next quarter.

Table 7.18

Year	Quarter	Time	Profit
1	1	1	17
1	2	2	23
1	3	3	5
1	4	4	4
2	1	5	21
2	2	6	26
2	3	7	7
2	4	8	6
3	1	9	22
3	2	10	24
3	3	11	6
3	4	12	5

3. A restaurant has begun offering a special 'early bird' menu on certain evenings. To avail of the offer, a table must be booked at 5pm, 6pm or 7pm. The number of tables booked at each hour, on the first four evenings of the initiative, is shown below. Forecast the number of bookings at each hour for the next evening.

Table 7.19

Day	Hour	Time	Bookings
1	5	1	10
1	6	2	12
1	7	3	16
2	5	4	14
2	6	5	22
2	7	6	22
3	5	7	16
3	6	8	22
3	7	9	30
4	5	10	23
4	6	11	34
4	7	12	39

4. Calculate the Laspeyres and Paasche price indices, the Laspeyres and Paasche quantity indices, the Fisher price and quantity indices, and the value index, for these fuel data.

Table 7.20

Year	p (Coal)	p (Gas)	q (Coal)	q (Gas)
1	145	98	53	20
2	150	105	56	12
3	160	108	50	32

5. Calculate the Laspeyres and Paasche price indices, the Laspeyres and Paasche quantity indices, the Fisher price and quantity indices, and the value index, for these transport data.

Table 7.21

Year	p (Rail)	p (Road)	q (Rail)	q (Road)
1	240	210	60	50
2	265	215	40	80
3	280	215	40	90

6. Calculate the Laspeyres and Paasche price indices, the Laspeyres and Paasche quantity indices, the Fisher price and quantity indices, and the value index, for these building materials data.

Table 7.22

Year	p (Wood)	p (Bricks)	q (Wood)	q (Bricks)
1	600	240	48	80
2	610	280	52	70
3	630	290	50	63

7. Two volume index-number series of industrial production, national and regional, are shown below. Change the base of the national index to year 1, and use the national index to deflate the regional index. Is the regional index outstripping the national one?

Table 7.23

Year	National	Regional
1	149.2	127.5
2	153.9	132.3
3	169.6	138.7
4	178.8	141.9

Curvilinear, Multiple and Logistic Regression

Curvilinear Regression

Sometimes a scatterplot reveals a **curvilinear relationship** between two variables.

Example: Different doses of a drug were administered to a number of patients and the responses were observed.

Fig 7.12

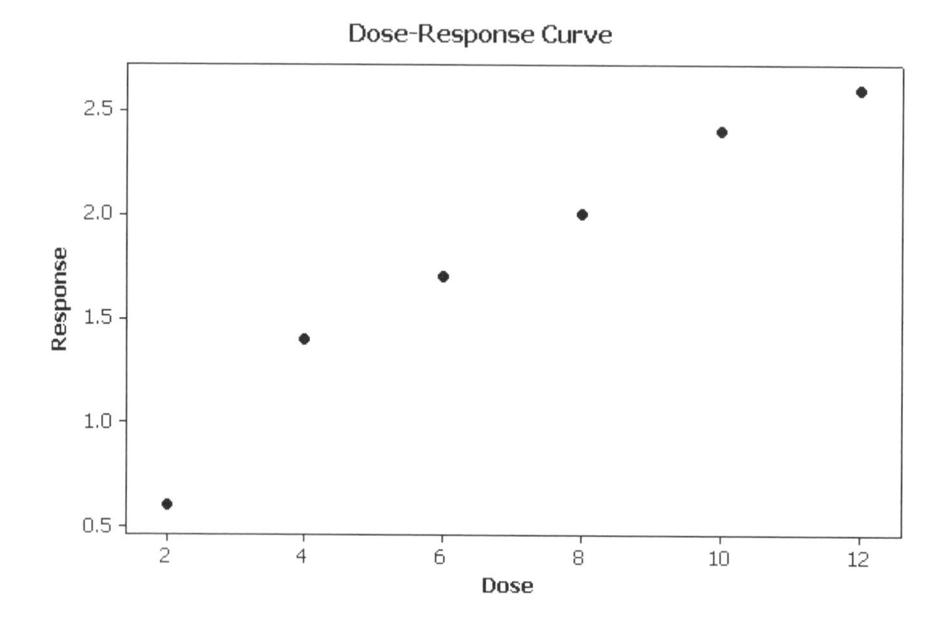

There are two different approaches that can be taken in these circumstances. The first approach is to fit the equation of a curve. A simple curve with a single elbow is described by a **quadratic equation**, so there is an additional **X**-squared term in the regression model.

Model 7.4

Quadratic Regression Model

$$Y = \alpha + \beta_1 X + \beta_2 X^2 + \epsilon$$

Fig 7.13

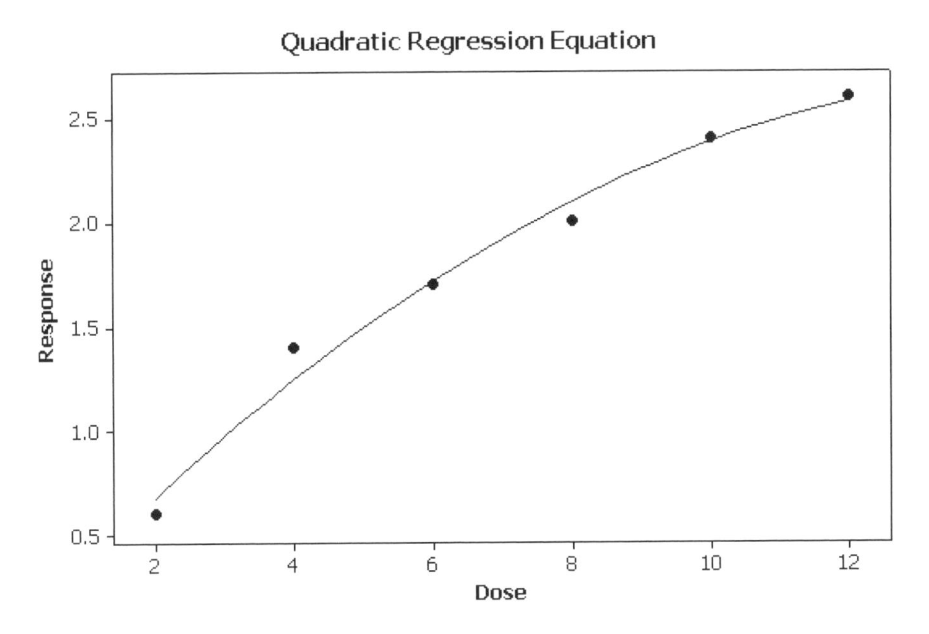

The regression equation is fitted using software:

Response = 0.0200 + 0.3525 Dose – 0.01161 Dose Squared.

The second approach is to straighten out the curve by using a suitable mathematical **transformation**. This is actually easier than it sounds. To begin with, the **X** variable is simply **X** itself, or X^1. This is called the **identity transformation**. We can **stretch** the **X**-axis by raising the power to X^2 or X^3. Or we can **shrink** the **X**-axis by using $\sqrt{X}$ or log **X** or X^{-1} or X^{-2}. The further the power is raised or lowered, the more stretching or shrinking occurs. In our example, the **X**-axis needs to be shrunk, so we try log **X**. We can use base 10, or any other base, for the logarithms.

Table 7.24

Dose	Response	Log (Dose)
2	0.6	0.30103
4	1.4	0.60206
6	1.7	0.77815
8	2.0	0.90309
10	2.4	1.00000
12	2.6	1.07918

Fig 7.14

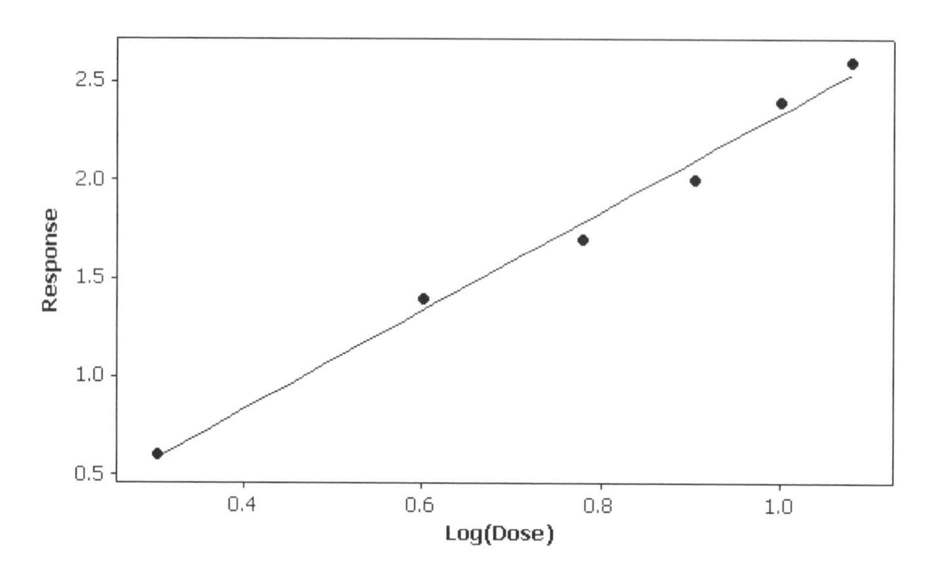

The regression equation is:

Response = −0.1721 + 2.516 Log(Dose)

We are now dealing with a familiar linear regression, and we can use all the usual techniques such as prediction intervals. Just be careful to remember that **X** now stands for log of dose and not dose itself, e.g. **X** = 1 corresponds to a dose of 10 units.

If you try a transformation that bends the curve too far, or not far enough, just try again. If you have a good knowledge of the underlying process, then you may be able to identify the appropriate transformation even before looking at the data. For example, if **X** is the diameter of an orange and **Y** is its weight, then X^3 is probably the correct transformation. Can you explain why? Also, the **Y** variable could be transformed instead of the **X** variable.

Multiple Regression

Sometimes more than one suitable predictor variable is available, and a **multiple regression** equation can be constructed. For example, the drying time of glue may be related to the moisture content of the glue (MC) and the relative humidity of the atmosphere (RH). The multiple regression equation is:

Drying = −15.9 + 2.17 MC + 0.975 RH

This is a linear equation in three dimensions, and could be represented by a **plane**. If quadratic terms were included, then the equation could represent a **response surface** with a peak or a ridge. It is interesting to compare this multiple regression equation to a simple regression equation that uses the same data.

Drying = −4.7 + 4.17 MC

The coefficient of MC is not the same in the two models. In the simple regression equation, it signifies that every one unit increase in MC is associated with an increase of 4.17 in the drying time. In the multiple regression equation, it signifies that every one unit increase in MC is associated with an increase of 2.17 in the drying time, **provided that the RH remains constant**.

There may be other variables that could also be used to predict the drying time, such as the ambient temperature and the thickness of the glue.

Table 7.25

Drying	MC	RH	Temp	Thick
121	29	71	16	3
116	26	74	23	2
107	25	57	14	4
92	23	56	20	3
83	18	60	23	3
100	23	57	15	3
61	22	39	15	3
107	27	72	16	4
98	25	61	21	3
81	25	66	19	3

We are now faced with a choice among a large number of regression models. We could use any one predictor variable, any two, any three or all four. How can we choose the **best subset** of predictors? A simple criterion is to choose the model that has the highest r^2 (adjusted) value. Software can be used to evaluate all possible subsets and to present the best candidates. The final headings in the table below should be read vertically. An **X** denotes a variable that is present in the model.

Table 7.26

Variables	R–Sq	R–Sq(adj)	s	MC	RH	Temp	Thick
1	60.3	55.3	12.033		X		
1	48.9	42.5	13.657	X			
2	68.8	59.9	11.405	X	X		
2	68.6	59.6	11.443		X	X	
3	70.2	55.4	12.030	X	X	X	
3	69.6	54.3	12.167		X	X	X
4	70.5	47.0	13.114	X	X	X	X

The highest r^2 (adjusted) value is 59.9%, suggesting that we should use the two-variable model with RH and MC. It may surprise you that the full model with four variables is not the best model. Every additional variable introduced into the model will seem to explain more of the variation in the sample – notice how the r^2 value keeps increasing. But a degree of freedom is lost every time a new variable is introduced, so it is better to use the statistic that is 'adjusted' for degrees of freedom. This identifies the model that seems to explain more of the variation in the population.

In the 'best subsets' approach, a large number of models are considered and the best-fitting model is selected. In such situations, it can happen that the selected model is a good fit to the sample data, but is a poor fit to the population. It is advisable to select a fresh data set to confirm the validity of the model. Alternatively, the initial data set can be randomly split in two: half the data are used to fit a model and the other half are used to validate the model.

Best-subsets analysis is a simple way to trawl through historical process data for clues about which inputs may be affecting an important response, such as yield.

Logistic Regression

We have used regression techniques to investigate relationships and to make estimates where **X** and **Y** are both measurements. We will now use shoe-size (**X**) to estimate gender (**Y**). This time, the response is an attribute (male = 1, female = 0).

Table 7.27

X	9	9	6	4	10	5	11	9	10	4	9	5	8	5	6	11	12	9	6	7
Y	1	1	0	0	1	0	1	0	1	0	1	0	1	0	0	1	1	1	0	0

Logistic regression uses the **logit** (i.e. the natural log of the odds) to transform the proportion into a response variable with a range from minus infinity to plus infinity. A regression equation is fitted using a technique called **maximum likelihood**.

Table 7.28

Predictor	Coef	SE Coef	Z	P	Odds Ratio
Constant	–15.6518	8.32372	–1.88	0.060	
Shoe-Size	1.95326	0.984379	1.98	0.047	7.05

The **p**-value for shoe-size (0.047) indicates that the parameter is not zero. The odds of a person being male increases by an estimated 7.05 times with every one unit increase in shoe-size. For example, the odds of someone with a size 11 shoe being male are 342 to 1. For a shoe-size of 8 or below, the odds favour a female.

Selection Table for Relationships

To select a statistical procedure for investigating a relationship between a response variable and a predictor variable, use this **selection table for relationships**. Enter the column according to the type of response variable, and go to the row that corresponds to the type of predictor variable.

Table 7.29

	Response is an attribute e.g. gender	**Response is a measurement e.g. height**
Predictor is an attribute e.g. shoe colour	Contingency Table	ANOVA
Predictor is a measurement e.g. shoe-size	Logistic Regression	Regression

Having completed this chapter you should be able to:

- investigate the relationship between two or more variables;
- use the values of predictor variables to estimate a response;
- forecast future values in a time series.

Problems 7.3

1. Plastic components experience shrinkage for some time after moulding. Use a curvilinear regression model to estimate the average shrinkage after seven minutes.

Table 7.30

Minutes	Shrinkage
5	2.5
10	3.4
15	3.8
20	4.4
25	4.9
30	5.4

2. The prices of a number of small cars are shown, along with information on the age, kilometres travelled and engine size. Identify the best subset of predictors for price, from among the available predictors: age, kilometres and engine.

Table 7.31

Price	Age	Kilometres	Engine
8250	4	20000	1.0
6995	5	106667	1.5
14795	0	8333	1.2
12750	1	25888	1.0
11750	2	21667	1.2
9950	3	28843	1.0
2500	9	158333	1.0
3750	8	175000	1.0
4900	7	85000	1.0
5950	6	108333	1.0

3. Use logistic regression to investigate whether the price of one of these cars is a useful indicator of whether or not its engine size is one litre.

8
PROCESSES

At the end of this chapter you will be able to:

- investigate the capability of a process;
- control processes, using appropriate SPC techniques;
- select and apply sampling plans;
- validate a measurement system.

A quality revolution occurred in the technology sector in the second half of the twentieth century. It was partly due to the application of statistical techniques to production and design processes. These statistical tools are now well established in the technology sector, and are being adopted more slowly in the administrative and service sectors, where the measurements of interest are less tangible. However, suitable measurements are available, such as time and cost. There is also an abundance of relevant attribute responses: an appointment is kept or not, a diagnosis is correct or not, a repair is effective or not, a server is courteous or not. Of course, there are some important things that cannot be measured directly, like the value of a satisfied customer. And there are certain difficulties with the application of statistical techniques to human behaviour, e.g. when a measure becomes a target it ceases to be a good measure (Goodhart's Law). However, used appropriately, statistical techniques can contribute to the investigation, control, validation and improvement of a wide variety of processes.

Process Capability

Measurements from every process exhibit some variation from the target response. It is useful to be able to identify the smallest variation that the process is capable of, and to consider whether this satisfies the specifications demanded by the customer or designer. Many processes are normally distributed and so the spread of measurements can be represented by a bell-shaped curve and expressed as: process capability $= \pm 3\sigma$.

But σ can have two different meanings in this context. A set of process measurements, collected all at once, gives an idea of the behaviour of the process at a snapshot in time. The standard deviation calculated **within** such a subgroup represents the **short-term** or inherent process variation. In reality, the process operates over an extended period of time, under different environmental conditions and with different lots of incoming material. These external influences can affect the **stability** of the process, causing the process mean to drift and shift. Therefore it is more realistic to collect a set of data over an extended period, and to simply calculate the **overall**, or **long-term**, standard deviation. The long-term variation includes the inherent variation and the time-to-time variation, i.e. the variation about the process mean and the variation of the process mean. A total of 150 data provides a good basis for a process capability study, and these could be collected as 30 subgroups of size 5. This allows both the overall (i.e. long-term) standard deviation and the pooled within-subgroups (i.e. short-term) standard deviation to be calculated. If the long-term standard deviation exceeds the short-term standard deviation by more than 10%, this confirms that time-to-time variation is present.

Example: A process fills bottles with a target volume of 120 ml. The lower and upper specification limits are: LSL = 115 ml and USL = 125 ml. Samples of size five were taken from thirty different batches as a basis for a process capability study.

Fig 8.1

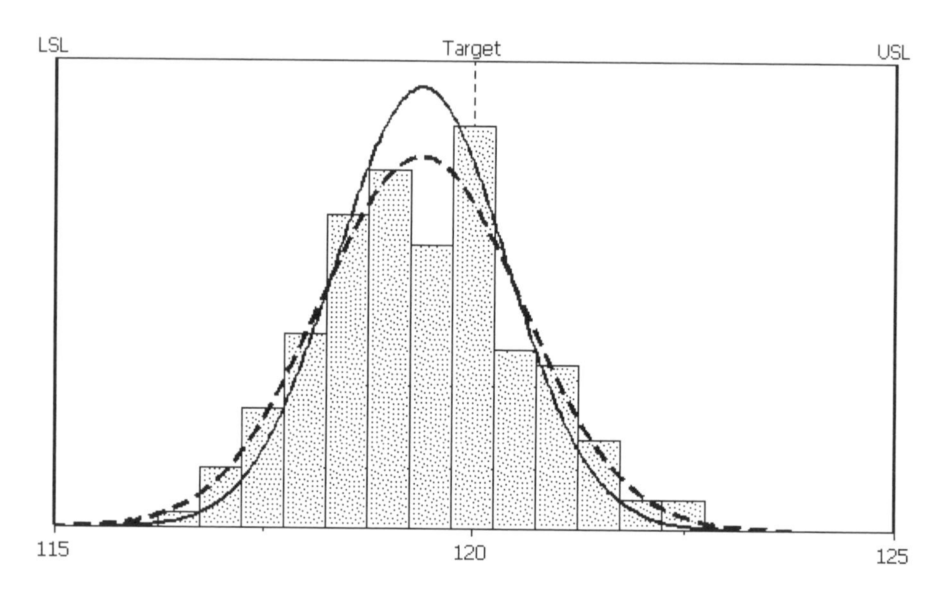

This graphical analysis fits a solid curve using the short-term standard deviation, and a wider, dashed curve using the long-term standard deviation. This is like viewing a bell-shaped vehicle from behind as it travels on a road between two fences (i.e. the specification limits). The solid curve is like a snapshot of the vehicle itself, showing that its width allows it to fit quite comfortably between the fences. The dashed curve is like a video of the vehicle, showing some additional side-to-side movement in its path as it travels. This gives us cause for concern that the road may not be wide enough after all.

The graph also highlights a new problem. The process is not centred. This can give rise to a violation at the nearest specification limit (NSL), even though the distance between the two specification limits is sufficiently wide. For some processes, it is a simple matter to correct this asymmetry by adjusting the process mean (μ) but for certain other processes, this is not simple at all.

A **process capability index** compares what the process is **required to do** (i.e. the specification range) to what the process is **able to do** (i.e. the spread of the process measurements). For the reasons already presented, the most realistic process capability index is the long-term, one-sided process capability index (P_{pk}).

P_{pk} long-term one-sided index
P_p long-term two-sided index
C_{pk} short-term one-sided index
C_p short-term two-sided index

Formula 8.1

Process Capability Indices

$$P_{pk} = \frac{|NSL - \mu|}{3\sigma}$$

$$P_p = \frac{USL - LSL}{6\sigma}$$

These formulae for **P_{pk}** and **P_p** use long-term σ.
The formulae for **C_{pk}** and **C_p** are identical but use short-term σ.

The relevant statistics and indices for the bottle-filling process are shown.

Table 8.1

Sample Mean	119.381
Standard Deviation (Overall)	1.198
Standard Deviation (Within)	1.011
P_{pk}	1.22
P_p	1.39
C_{pk}	1.44
C_p	1.65

It is generally regarded that 1.33 is the minimum acceptable value of a process capability index, for a process to be deemed capable. A value of 2 or greater is considered ideal.

Problems 8.1

1. The target duration of a castle tour is 45 minutes. The LSL and USL are 35 and 55 respectively. Five tours were timed on each of thirty days, and the following statistics were calculated.
   Sample Mean, 45.83
   Standard Deviation (Within), 1.99
   Standard Deviation (Overall), 2.02
   Estimate P_{pk}.
2. (Exercise) Place a ruler about a metre away from you, but with the graduations visible. Now take a pencil and a blank sheet of paper and draw a freehand line to a target length of 100 mm. Hide your first attempt and draw another freehand line. Repeat until you have a subgroup of five lines. Take a break for about one minute. Now repeat the whole activity until you have thirty subgroups, giving a total of 150 lines.
   Measure each line with the ruler. Calculate the sample mean and the overall standard deviation of the 150 lines (the long-term standard deviation). Complete your process capability study by calculating the long-term process capability indices, with respect to the LSL of 80 mm and the USL of 120 mm.

Process Control: SPC Charts

Statistical process control (SPC) observes the process to confirm that it **is doing** its best, or to see whether adjustments are required. Samples of process measurements are drawn at regular intervals and some sample statistic is plotted as a time series on the SPC chart. **Control limits** are also shown on the chart. These are not specification limits: they represent values that are unlikely to be violated ($p = 0.001$ approximately) as long as the process remains **in control**.

Ideally, measurements are made on the process rather than the product, since the product will be right if the process is right. For example, in the seasoning of timber, SPC would be applied to the kiln temperature, rather than to the moisture content of the finished timber. This facilitates timely intervention: if the process goes **out of control**, and prompt corrective action is taken, the product will be OK. The idea is to correct problems before any defective units are produced. Even if a defective unit of product does occur, the focus of SPC is not on fixing that unit, but on identifying the cause and taking action to prevent any recurrence of the same problem.

Small variations in process measurements are inevitable. SPC charts distinguish between these small variations, due to **common causes**, and more serious variations due to **special causes**. Common causes include the many small, unavoidable changes in the environment and the process that give rise to normally distributed process measurements. A special cause is a single factor that has a large impact on the process, and that must be identified and dealt with. Special causes will typically be one of the 6 Ms:

Men, e.g. untrained or unmotivated workers
Material, e.g. defective or different material being used
Machines, e.g. damage, maladjustment, or overdue maintenance
Methods, e.g. procedures are inappropriate, unspecified or ignored
Milieu (environment), e.g. weather, utilities
Measurements, e.g. the measurement system may be giving false or erratic signals.

When an SPC chart gives an out-of-control signal, it cannot tell us what has caused the problem. We must use our knowledge of the process to interpret the SPC chart, and to pursue the cause and the solution. The time at which a signal appeared on the chart is a useful clue, although a problem often avoids detection until a number of samples have been taken. Sometimes an out-of-control signal points to an improvement, e.g. the waiting time or the number of defectives may have fallen. In such instances the cause should be identified and action taken to ensure recurrence, and new control limits should be calculated to reflect the improved capability of the process.

Individuals Chart

An **individuals chart** is the simplest control chart. Individual process measurements, assumed normally distributed, are sampled and plotted.

Formula 8.2

Control Limits for Individuals Chart

$$Limits = \mu \pm 3\sigma$$

Example: Customers at a drive-thru restaurant are sampled and the delay experienced by these customers is recorded in seconds. For the first 30 customers sampled, the data were as follows:

153, 171, 163, 164, 160, 134, 162, 149, 140, 186, 149, 139, 129, 147, 141, 152, 169, 150, 127, 138, 158, 135, 140, 172, 161, 158, 155, 144, 177, 211

The estimated process mean and standard deviation are 154.47 and 17.98 respectively.

Fig 8.2

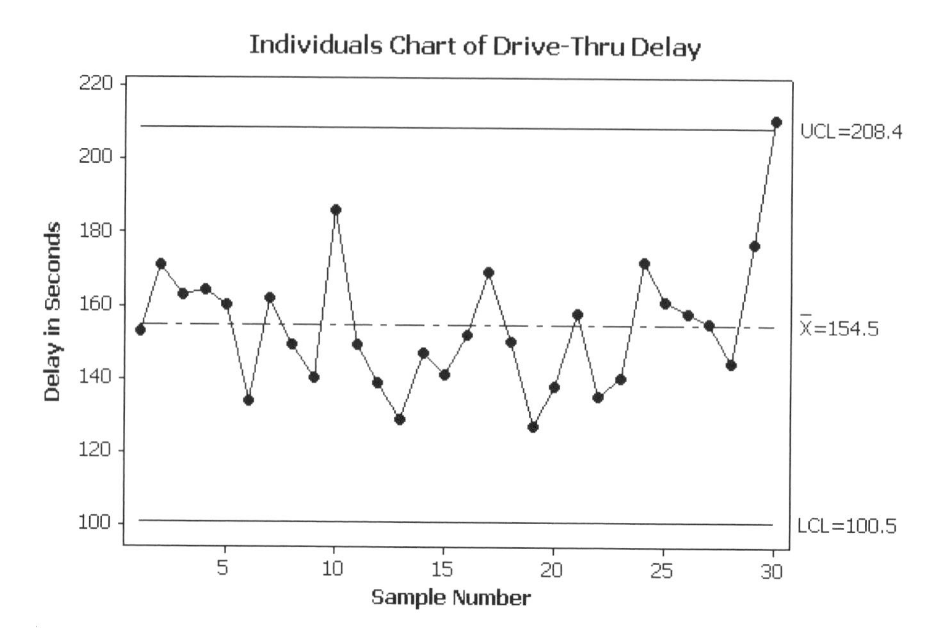

The final point indicates that the process is out of control. The reason could be a new, inexperienced worker (men), a specialised order (material), a broken drink dispenser (machines), failure to submit the food order before pouring drinks (methods), a reduction in electrical power (milieu), or measuring the time until the customer drives away rather than until the order is delivered (measurements). The cause must be identified and corrected. If the USL is 240 seconds, then corrective action can be taken before any defective units are produced. New sample data can be simply plotted on the chart as they arise.

Xbar Chart

An **Xbar chart** uses a plot of sample means to track the process mean. The process measurements do not need to be normally distributed. The specification limits for individual values must not be shown on the chart, or compared with values on the chart, because these are sample means.

Formula 8.3

Control Limits for Xbar Chart

$$Limits = \mu \pm 3\frac{\sigma}{\sqrt{n}}$$

The estimated process mean and the long-term standard deviation should be used to calculate realistic long-term control limits.

Example: Samples of five bottles each were taken from thirty different batches of a filling process, and the fill volume was observed in each case. The overall sample mean and standard deviation were 119.381 ml and 1.198 ml respectively.

Fig 8.3

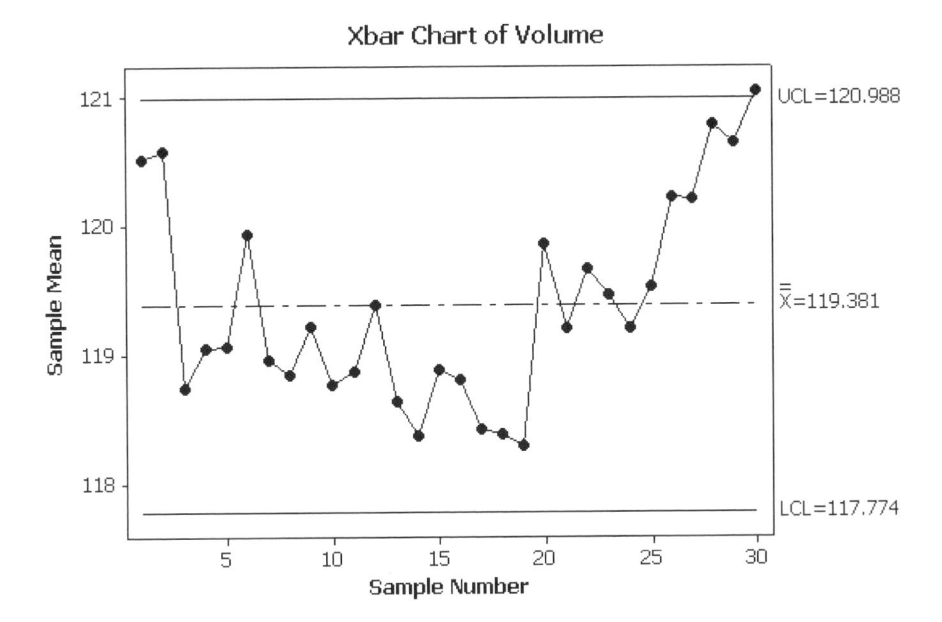

The final point indicates that the process is out of control. Can you suggest one or more possible causes?

Sample standard deviation charts, **s charts**, or sample range charts, **R charts**, are sometimes used to accompany Xbar charts. These charts give a signal when the spread of values rises or falls significantly.

np Chart

We now consider control charts for attributes. The number of **defectives** in a sample can be monitored using an **np chart**. This involves drawing a sample of fixed size, **n**, at regular intervals, counting the number of defectives in the sample, and plotting this number on the chart. The parameter **p** represents the proportion defective in the process, and this can be estimated from the data. Sample sizes must be large, because an average of at least 5 defectives per sample is required. Violation of an upper control limit indicates an increase in the proportion of defective units, but violation of a lower control limit indicates improvement in the process. The limits are based on the normal approximation to the binomial distribution.

Formula 8.4

Control Limits for np Chart

$$Limits = np \pm 3\sqrt{np(1-p)}$$

Example: The proportion of late deliveries made by an office-products supplier is monitored by sampling 50 deliveries each day and counting how many of these were late. The results for thirty consecutive days were as follows:

8, 11, 6, 12, 6, 8, 10, 16, 9, 8, 10, 7, 8, 15, 11, 15, 10, 4, 11, 15, 11, 7, 5, 9, 8, 7, 8, 6, 12, 11

Total late deliveries = 284
Average number late per sample = 284/30 = 9.47
Estimated proportion late, **p** = 9.47/50 = 0.1894

Fig 8.4

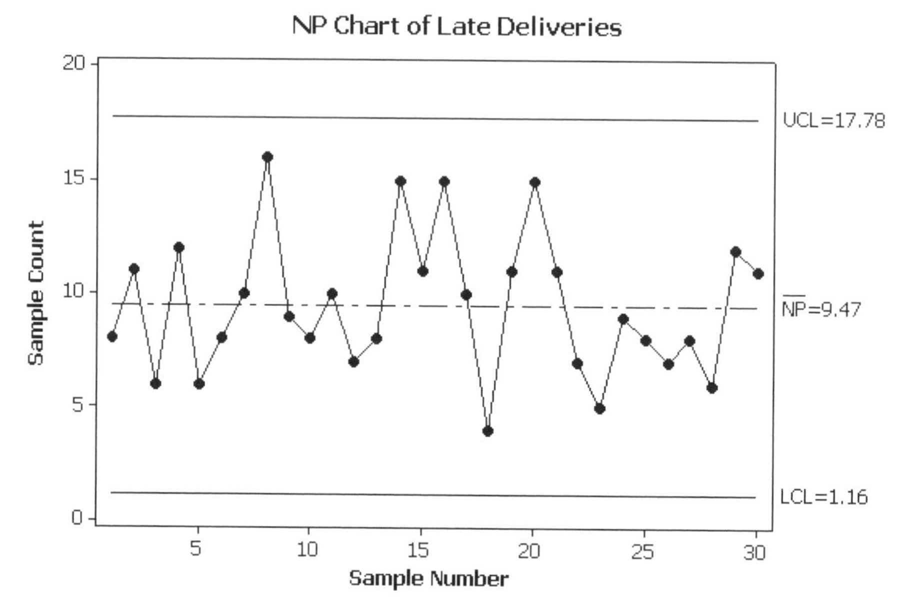

The chart indicates that the process is in control. This means that the behaviour of the process is consistent, even if the proportion of defectives is high.

c Chart

The next attribute control chart, the **c chart**, tracks the number of **defects** in a sample. The sample must be defined: it could be a unit of product, a number of units, an interval of time, a length, an area, a volume or a mass. The number of defects in the sample (e.g. scratches, leaks, missed calls) is plotted on the chart.

The parameter λ represents the average number of defects per sample, and this can be estimated from the data. Sample sizes must be large, because an average of at least 5 defects per sample is required. Violation of an upper control limit indicates an increase in the level of defects, but violation of a lower control limit indicates improvement in the process. The limits are based on the normal approximation to the Poisson distribution.

Formula 8.5

Control Limits for c Chart

$$Limits = \lambda \pm 3\sqrt{\lambda}$$

Example: The number of suitcases damaged at an airport each day was recorded for thirty consecutive days, with the following results:

17, 22, 21, 22, 20, 8, 19, 13, 23, 22, 11, 16, 21, 14, 19, 16, 13, 14, 11, 16, 14, 12, 13, 21, 11, 16, 11, 16, 14, 3

Total number of damaged suitcases = 469
Average number damaged per day = 15.63

Fig 8.5

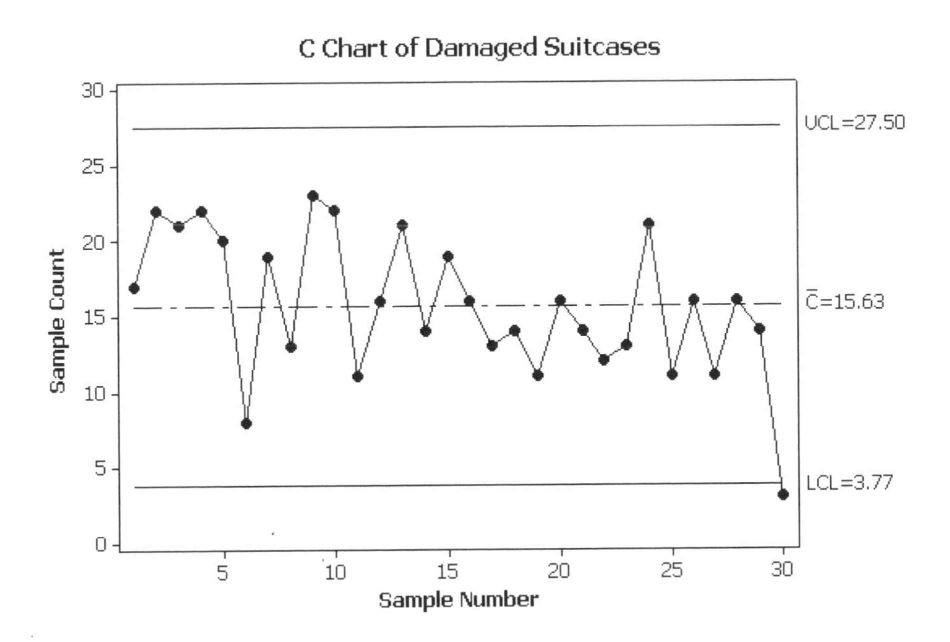

The chart indicates that the process has improved. The cause should be identified and action taken to ensure recurrence.

Setting up an SPC System

The questions to be addressed when setting up an SPS system are outlined below.

1. Which process parameter needs to be controlled?

In a filling process, the critical parameter could be the volume, the weight, or the proportion of bottles that are underfull.

2. Which statistics should be plotted?

A chart for controlling volume could plot individual volumes, sample means, or sample means and standard deviations.

3. How big should the sample be?

Small samples of about five measurements, drawn frequently, facilitate a rapid response to problems.

4. How will the samples be drawn?

Samples should form **rational subgroups**. The units within a sample should be as alike as possible, so they should be taken close together in time and not mixed from different sources.

5. How often will samples be drawn?

For a process that is prone to shift suddenly out of specification, the economic principle is: if defective product is costing more than inspection, then inspect more frequently. In the case of a process that drifts at a predictable rate, the sampling frequency should ensure that the process is visited before it drifts out of specification.

6. How will the control limits be calculated?

It is usual to estimate the parameters from the process data, and use these values to calculate the control limits. An alternative approach is to use target parameter values when calculating the limits, but this can lead to either of two problems. Firstly, if the process is not achieving the target standard, there will be multiple violations on the SPC chart and no corrective actions may be available. Secondly, if the process is performing to a higher standard than required, the level of control will be relaxed, and process improvement opportunities will not be noticed.

7. What response will be made to an out-of-control signal?

This is the most important question. The purpose of control charts is to provoke action to deal with causes as required. Action must be taken. The action should always be visible to the personnel who maintain the control charts, so that they remain motivated.

PROBLEMS 8.2

1. Five castle tours were timed on each of thirty days, and the following statistics were calculated.
   Sample Mean, 45.83 minutes
   Standard Deviation (Overall), 2.02
   Calculate control limits for an individuals chart, and also for an Xbar chart with sample size 5.
2. (Exercise) Use the sample mean and the overall standard deviation of the 150 lines drawn earlier (see problems 8.1 #2) to calculate control limits for an Xbar chart with sample size 5. Draw the chart and plot the thirty sample means on the chart. What does the chart reveal about the process?
3. The historical proportion of 'false positive' diagnoses at a screening clinic is 0.06. Calculate limits for an **np** chart with a sample size of 100.
4. The average number of scratches on a polarising filter screen is 10. Calculate limits for a **c** chart where a sample consists of one of these filter screens.

Sampling Inspection

Sampling inspection by attributes provides a method for validating a series of batches from a process. It confirms that what the process has done satisfies stated requirements.

Of course, it is better to manufacture products **right first time** rather than using resources to inspect out the bad units afterwards. If it is inevitable that some defective units will be made, then effective 100% inspection can be used to identify and remove all of these defectives. If 100% inspection is too costly, then sampling inspection can be used to ensure that the level of defectives is not too high.

Sampling Plans

Sampling inspection is carried out by following a **sampling plan**. A sampling plan consists of a rule for selecting the sample and a rule for making a decision based on the sample.

Example: Sampling Plan: **n** = 8, **Ac** 1, **Re** 2.

This plan calls for a random sample of 8 units to be selected from the batch and inspected. If one or fewer defectives are found in the sample, then all the rest of the batch is accepted. If two or more defectives are found in the sample, then the entire batch is rejected. Rejected batches undergo **rectification**, which involves 100% inspection and replacement of all defectives by non-defectives.

How Sampling Plans Work

Whether or not a particular batch will be accepted depends partly on the quality of the batch, and partly on the luck of the draw. The quality of the batch is measured by the proportion of defectives (**p**) in the batch, called the **incoming quality level**. For any given value of **p**, there is a certain chance that the batch will be accepted, called the **probability of acceptance** (P_A). The probability of acceptance is the proportion of all such batches that would be accepted, in the long run.

For a 'good' batch, with only 5% defective, P_A = 94% with this sampling plan. The producer and consumer might have agreed in advance that any value of **p** up to 5% is acceptable as a process average. This figure, the highest acceptable process average per cent defective, is called the **acceptable quality level** (AQL). Batches that have a proportion defective equal to the AQL should be accepted, and we see that 94% of such batches are accepted. The remaining 6% of such batches are simply unfortunate: their samples of 8 units just happen to contain two or more defective units, although the proportion defective in the batch is only 5%. Hence, the probability of rejection in such a case (6%, in this example) is called the **producer's risk** (α). Note that the AQL does not specify the maximum acceptable per cent defective in a batch, but the average acceptable per cent defective in the process. Therefore, many individual batches with per cent defective higher than the AQL may happen to be accepted.

For a 'bad' batch, with 40% defective, P_A = 11% with this sampling plan. The producer and consumer might have agreed in advance that 40% defective is unacceptable even in a single batch. Such a figure is called the **lot tolerance per cent defective** (LTPD), or **limiting quality** (LQ), or **rejectable quality level** (RQL). Batches with a proportion defective equal to the LTPD should not be accepted, and we see that only 11% of such batches are accepted. These 11% are fortunate: their samples of 8 units just happen to contain fewer than two defective units, although the proportion defective in the batch is 40%. Hence, the probability of acceptance in this case (11%, in this example) is called the **consumer's risk** (β).

What Sampling Plans Do

What can sampling plans do for us? Firstly, sampling plans can identify a very bad batch (LTPD or worse) immediately. Secondly, sampling plans can identify an unacceptable process (worse than AQL) sooner or later: as batches from such a process are frequently submitted for sampling inspection, some of them will eventually get caught.

What can sampling plans not do for us? Firstly, sampling plans cannot take the place of corrective action: when batches are rejected because of poor quality, corrective action is essential – just continuing with sampling inspection is a waste of time. Secondly, sampling plans cannot guarantee a correct decision about any one particular batch. Thirdly, sampling plans can not ensure **zero defects**: either 'right first time' or effective, 100% inspection is required for this.

Sampling Plan Calculations

Let **n**, **p** and **c** represent the sample size, the incoming quality level, and the acceptance number, respectively. The probability of acceptance is the probability of obtaining **c** or fewer defectives. This is the cumulative probability of **c** for a binomial distribution with parameters **n** and **p**.

The table below shows the probability of acceptance, corresponding to a number of different values of the incoming quality level, for the sampling plan **n** = 8, **Ac** 1, **Re** 2.

Table 8.2

p (%)	P_A
0	1
5	0.9428
10	0.8131
15	0.6572
20	0.5033
25	0.3671
30	0.2553
35	0.1691
40	0.1064
45	0.0632
100	0

A graph of P_A versus **p** is called an **operating characteristic curve**.

Figure 8.6

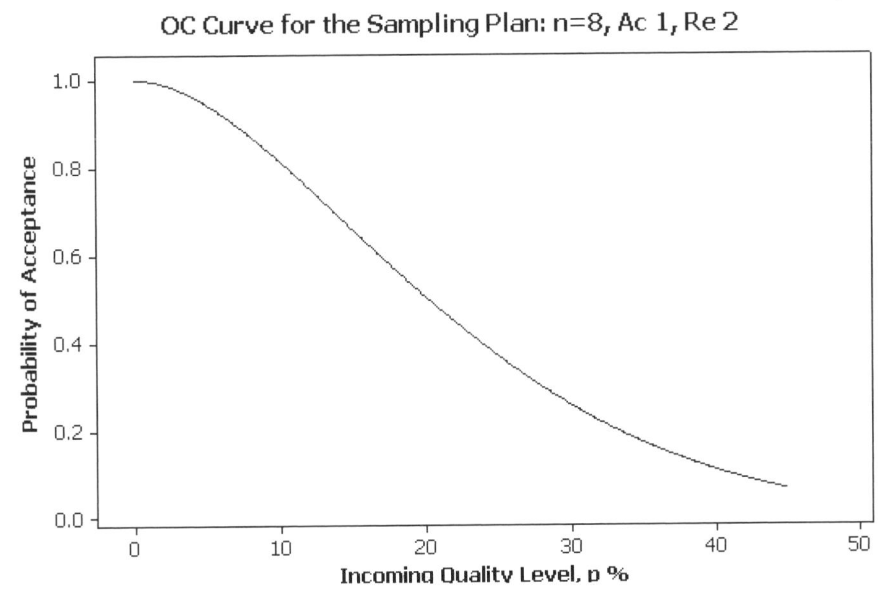

The OC curve is very useful. It shows the level of protection that the plan offers against any value of the incoming quality level. Before selecting a sampling plan for use, its OC curve should be studied, to see if it is satisfactory. For example, the above plan could be useful in a situation where the LTPD is 40%, because P_A = 11%, but it would not be useful if the LTPD was 20%, because P_A = 50%. The value of p (p = 20% in this case) that has a probability of acceptance of 50% is called the **indifferent quality level**.

Outgoing Quality

Average outgoing quality (AOQ) is the proportion of defective parts downstream from sampling inspection. If no rectification is carried out on the rejected batches, then AOQ is only marginally better than the incoming quality level. (The rejected batches are removed, and in the case of accepted batches, any defective part found while sampling is replaced.) If rectification is carried out, the AOQ is better than the incoming quality level of the submitted batches. Theoretically, AOQ is low when incoming quality is very good and also when incoming quality is very poor, because this causes a great amount of 100% inspection. The peak on the AOQ curve is known as the **average outgoing quality limit** (AOQL). The AOQL provides a 'worst case' guarantee for the average outgoing quality of a continuous series of batches from a stable process, assuming that a rectification scheme is in place. Typically, the AOQL is marginally greater than the AQL if large samples are used. If the sampling plan uses smaller samples, the AOQL may be around two or three times the AQL.

Double Sampling Plans

Double sampling involves taking two smaller samples rather than one sample. If the first sample is very good or very bad, the batch can be accepted or rejected straight away, without any need for a second sample. Otherwise the second sample is drawn and a verdict is reached based on the cumulative sample. The advantage of double-sampling plans is that they typically involve smaller sample sizes. The disadvantages are that they are more complex to operate and in some situations it can be very troublesome to have to return for a second sample. **Multiple-sampling** plans are similar to double-sampling plans, but involve taking up to seven small samples: after each sample it may be possible to make a decision about the batch without drawing any further samples. **Sequential sampling** takes this concept to the limit: after each sampling unit is drawn, a decision is made to accept the batch, to reject the batch, or to continue sampling.

Practical Guidelines for Sampling Plans

Before choosing a sampling plan, the AQL and the LTPD must be identified. On this book's website, alongside the data sets, you can find a **sampling plan calculator**. This is a tool that will automatically produce a sampling plan for any suitable values of the AQL and LTPD that you provide. Alternatively, published tables can be consulted to find a sampling plan that corresponds to your requirements.

For any given AQL value, the larger the LTPD value, the smaller the sample will be. Also if the batches are large, fewer samples are needed, but if a large batch fails there is a large rectification task to be completed. These things are useful to know if you are in a position to choose the LTPD or the batch size.

All samples should be drawn randomly from the entire batch, and this includes the first and second samples in a double-sampling plan. Avoid sampling only from the start of a run, or selecting clusters of units that are packaged together. Any compromising of random sampling reduces the level of protection by an uncertain amount, and makes your conclusions more dependent on the assumption that the process is stable.

PROBLEMS 8.3

1. Find a suitable sampling plan for the inspection of bandages if AQL = 2% and LTPD = 10%.
2. Find a suitable sampling plan for the inspection of misspelt names if AQL = 5% and LTPD = 15%.
3. A sampling plan for printed cartons is as follows:
   n = 13, **Ac** 0, **Re** 1.
   (a) What is the producer's risk if the AQL = 1%?
   (b) What is the consumer's risk if the LTPD = 20%?
   (c) If the incoming quality level is 3%, what is the probability of rejection?
   (d) If the incoming quality level is stable at 3%, what is the probability of a rejection occurring within the first six samples?
   (e) Construct the OC curve for this sampling plan and use it to determine the indifferent quality level.

Measurement System Validation

Accuracy and Precision

A measuring instrument can be tested by repeatedly measuring a fixed quantity, and comparing the results with the correct answer. The instrument is said to be **accurate** (unbiased) if the mean is on target. It is said to be **precise** if the standard deviation is small. i.e. the results are close together.

Example: A person who weighs 75 kg is weighed repeatedly on a scale. Any of the following patterns could arise.

Figure 8.7

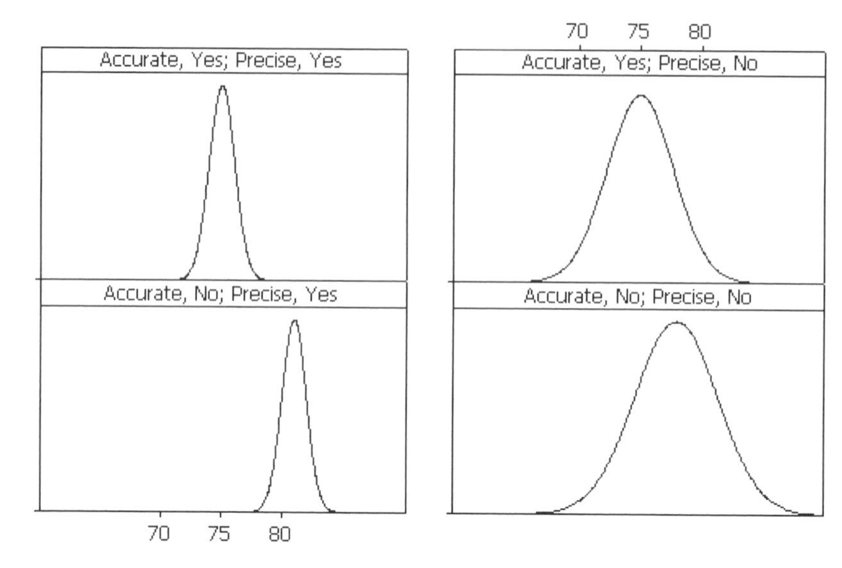

Gauge Linearity and Bias Studies

A linearity and bias study estimates the average **bias** of an instrument, and investigates whether the bias changes as bigger objects are measured (**linearity**). In this context, the instrument is often referred to as a **gauge**, and the objects are referred to as **parts**.

A number of parts are selected, covering the full range of the instrument. The **master measurement** for each part is obtained from a trusted authority such as a reference laboratory or an expert opinion. Then each part is measured a number of times with the instrument. The individual deviation of each measurement from its master is calculated, and also the average deviation for each part.

Example: A kitchen scale was tested by weighing five consumer products a number of times each.

Table 8.3

Part	Master	Measurement	Deviation	Average Deviation
1	200	260 270	60 70	65.0
2	300	375 340	75 40	57.5
3	400	500 505	100 105	102.5
4	625	725 740	100 115	107.5
5	700	780 790	80 90	85.0

The mean of all the individual deviations is the average bias.

Average bias = 83.5

This scale tends to overstate the weight by 83.5 grams on average.

To estimate the linearity, we find the regression equation of average deviation on master.

The regression equation is:

Average Deviation = 53.5 + 0.0673 Master

Multiply the slope by 100 to get the %Linearity.

%Linearity = +6.73%

For every 100 units increase in the master measurement, the bias tends to increase by 6.73 units.

Components of Variance

When a set of parts are measured, the total variation arises from **material variation** (the parts are not all the same) and variation due to the **measurement system** (i.e. the set of instruments and operators that take the measurements). These two sources of variation are assumed to be independent, so the following model applies.

Model 8.1

$$\sigma^2_{Total} = \sigma^2_{Mat} + \sigma^2_{MS}$$

It may be possible to explain some of the measurement system variation by pointing out that the measurements arose on different **sessions** i.e. different operators, different instruments, or different days. But even on a single session, there may be some unexplained variation. The standard deviation between sessions is called **reproducibility** (rpd) and the standard deviation within sessions is called **repeatability** (rpt). These two sources of variation are assumed to be independent.

Model 8.2

$$\sigma^2_{MS} = \sigma^2_{rpd} + \sigma^2_{rpt}$$

Care should be taken that any subtle material variation, is not attributed to the measurement system. Examples include time-to-time variation, such as shrinkage, or within-part variation, such as different diameters on the same part.

The complete model attributes variation to three sources: differences between parts (material variation), differences between sessions (reproducibility), and unexplained variation (repeatability).

Model 8.3

$$\sigma^2_{Total} = \sigma^2_{Mat} + \sigma^2_{rpd} + \sigma^2_{rpt}$$

Gauge R&R Studies

An **R&R study** is a designed experiment, in which a number of typical parts are measured a number of times in succession (to investigate repeatability), on a number of different sessions (to investigate reproducibility). If measurement is destructive, replication can be achieved by using indestructible surrogate parts, or sub-samples of very similar parts.

Example: A measurement system is used to measure the deflection of timber beams, for which LSL = 20 mm and USL = 100 mm. An R&R study involved measuring 15 randomly chosen beams twice each, on each of four days. This involved taking 120 measurements; 30 on each session; 8 on each part.

This always leads to a two-factor experiment in which the response is 'measurement' and the factors are 'part' and 'session'. A preliminary ANOVA with interaction can be used to confirm that there is no significant interaction. (This would mean that some parts gave higher results in a particular session.) The main analysis consists of an additive, two-way ANOVA table.

Table 8.4

Two-way ANOVA: Measurement versus Part, Session

Source	DF	SS	MS	F	P
Part	14	1982.98	141.641	19.21	0.000
Session	3	6.52	2.174	0.29	0.829
Error	102	752.14	7.374		
Total	119	2741.64			

It is to be expected that the **p**-value for part will be significant, but it would be an immediate worry if the **p**-value for session was significant.

The **variance components** can be estimated from the ANOVA table as follows.

Error (Repeatability): 7.374
Session (Reproducibility): (2.174 – 7.374)/30 = −0.1733
Since a variance cannot be negative, we adjust this estimate to zero. The estimated variance component for the measurement system is 7.374 + 0 = 7.374
Part (Material): (141.641 – 7.374)/8 = 16.7834
The corresponding standard deviation estimates are:
Repeatability: 2.71549
Reproducibility: 0
Measurement System: 2.71549
Material: 4.09676

These standard deviation estimates are used to compute the **signal-to-noise ratio** (SNR) and the %R&R.

Formula 8.6

$$SNR = \frac{\sigma_{mat}}{\sigma_{MS}}$$

The SNR asks whether the measurement system is able to tell the difference between the parts that are presented to it.
Threshold values for the SNR are as follows:

>10: good
3–10: acceptable
<3: unacceptable

In this case:

SNR = 4.09676 / 2.71549 = 1.5

This is unacceptable. The measurement system is unable to tell between the parts that are presented to it. However, this may be because the parts are very alike. Strangely, as production processes improve, the SNR goes down: it appears that the measurement system is deteriorating when in fact the parts are simply more alike, and therefore it is more difficult to tell them apart.

Although the measurement system cannot tell between the parts that are presented to it, it may be able to tell the difference between a good part and a bad part. The %R&R (also called the **precision to tolerance ratio**) asks how well the instrument can distinguish between good and bad parts.

Formula 8.7

$$\%R\&R = \frac{6 \times \sigma_{MS}}{USL - LSL} \times 100$$

Threshold values for the %R&R are as follows:

< 10%: good
10–30%: acceptable
>30%: unacceptable
In the example above, USL − LSL = 80
%R&R = (6 × 2.71549) / 80 × 100 = 20.4%

This measurement system is able to distinguish between good and bad parts.

If a measurement system is inadequate, what can be done about it? First, identify whether reproducibility or repeatability is contributing more variation. If reproducibility is the main problem, corrective action could include training (if sessions denote different operators), or calibration (if sessions denote different instruments). If the main problem is repeatability there may be no simple solution: perhaps the instrument is simply not good enough.

Attribute Gauge R&R Studies

An **attribute measurement system** consists of instruments (such as **go/no-go gauges**) or human inspectors that make judgments to either accept or reject parts that are considered to be good or bad. Samples of both good and bad parts are inspected at least twice (to assess repeatability) by at least two instruments or inspectors (to assess reproducibility). For automated test systems, reusable test parts can be colour coded to facilitate easy identification of their status, but for human inspectors the parts must be disguised and presented in a newly randomised order each time. The master classification of the test parts as good or bad must be based on an objective or trusted standard.

Example: Fifty biscuits (31 good and 19 bad) were presented twice, in random order, to two inspectors (Evan and Silvia) who were required to judge their colour acceptability. An extract from the results is shown below: 1 denotes good or accept, while 0 denotes bad or reject.

Table 8.5

Part	Master	Evan 1	Evan 2	Silvia 1	Silvia 2	Outcome
1	1	1	1	1	1	Effective
2	0	0	0	0	0	Effective
3	1	1	1	1	0	Rpt
4	1	0	0	1	1	Rpd
5	1	0	0	0	0	Bias

Rows 1 and 2 show the measurement system working effectively. Row 3 shows evidence of a problem with repeatability: at least one inspector was inconsistent. Row 4 shows evidence of a reproducibility problem: all inspectors were consistent, but two inspectors disagreed. Row 5 shows evidence of a bias problem: all inspectors were consistent and all inspectors agreed, but their classification was wrong. A simple way to summarise the data is to indicate the percentage of rows from the complete data set that fell into each category.
Effective: 80% (40 rows)
Repeatability: 10% (5 rows)

Reproducibility: 8% (4 rows)
Bias: 2% (1 row)

Remedial actions can include training and communication (for bias and reproducibility problems), and the provision of specimens at the inspection station that are just inside the threshold of acceptability (for repeatability problems).

A larger sample size can be achieved by passing the same parts through the measurement system again, provided that the inspection errors are independent of the parts. In fact, during normal operation of an inspection process, duplicate inspection (**200% inspection**) offers a simple but labour-intensive method for increasing the reliability of test results.

Biases are of two types, false positive (rejected but good) or false negative (accepted but bad) results. During normal inspection, false positive results tend to occur much more frequently, because the vast majority of incoming parts are good. False negative results are much more costly, because they lead to shipment or assembly of a bad part, resulting in mission failure, high field-repair costs and loss of reputation.

Having completed this chapter you should be able to:

- investigate the capability of a process, and quote a suitable process capability index to compare the long-term or short-term process variation with the specification limits;
- monitor the behaviour of a process by plotting measurement or attribute data on an appropriate SPC chart, and recognise signals that call for corrective action;
- select and apply a sampling plan to validate the acceptability of a series of batches from a process;
- assess the suitability of instruments for providing measurements or making classifications, and identify how particular measurement systems can be improved.

PROBLEMS 8.4

1. A map was used to estimate a number of actual distances in kilometres. Conduct a gauge linearity and bias study using the data below.

Table 8.6

Part	Master	Measurement
1	10	8 9
2	20	16 19
3	30	29 27
4	40	38 36
5	50	45 47

2. Suzanne carried out a Gauge R&R study in which three operators each measured twelve parts three times using a vision system. The parts had LSL = 42 mm and USL = 48 mm. Use the ANOVA table below to calculate the SNR and the %R&R.

Table 8.7

Two-way ANOVA: Measurement versus Part, Session

Source	DF	SS	MS	F	P
Part	11	207.293	18.8448	746.25	0.000
Session	2	2.793	1.3966	55.30	0.000
Error	94	2.374	0.0253		
Total	107	212.460			

3. Two inspectors, David and Emmanuel, each made two judgments on the quality of thirty grass surfaces, as part of an attribute gauge R&R study. Do any rows in the data extract below indicate a problem with repeatability, reproducibility or bias?

Table 8.8

Part	Master	David 1	David 2	Emmanuel 1	Emmanuel 2
1	0	0	0	0	0
2	0	0	0	1	1
3	0	0	1	1	0
4	0	0	0	0	0
5	0	1	1	1	1

Appendix 1
ANSWERS TO PROBLEMS

ANSWERS 1.1

1. (a) Bimodal. Gender differences.
   (b) Normal. Roughly equal quantities.
   (c) Truncated. Minimum line rental charge.
   (d) Skewed to the right. Minimum of zero but large maximum.
   (e) Truncated. Attendance cannot exceed seating capacity.
   (f) Normal. Roughly equal measurements.
   (g) Bimodal. Children and adults.
2. (a) Heating turned on. Weather gets progressively warmer. After each class period, doors are open and the room cools down.
   (b) Bad mid-term results provoke a surge in attendance. Attendance increases as exams draw near. Weekly cycle with low attendance on Fridays.
   (c) A large factory opens or closes. Growing residential area. Higher demand for electricity during winter months.
3. Bimodal. Mixture of shop-only customers and petrol customers.
4. Truncated. The tablets are nominally 400 g. Most tablets are overweight. Unacceptably overweight tablets have been removed by inspection.

ANSWERS 1.2

1. (a) None of the first 50 passengers has difficulty being in time for the train.
   (b) The interviewer is unlikely to choose to call at a home displaying a 'Beware of the Dog' sign! Would you?
   (c) The ten stalks all experienced 'edge of field' conditions of soil, irrigation, light, etc.
   (d) The first word on each page is more likely to be part of a heading, and may not be representative of normal text.
2. Assign 1 to Mirabelle, 2 to Kaitlin, etc. **N** = 9. Say **X** = 0.323. Then **i** = INT(9 × 0.323 + 1) = INT(3.907) = 3, so choose Sarah. Repeat until 3 are chosen.

Answers 1.3

1. (a) mean 8, sd 1
   (b) mean 8, sd 3.633
   (c) mean 28.85, sd 6.71
   (d) mean 27.14, sd 17.95 (using raw data)
   (e) mean 406.68, sd 2.09 (using raw data)
   (f) mean 4.296, sd 2.250
2. (a) The median. (b) The mode. (c) The mean.

Answers 2.1

1. (a) If the die is rolled many times, then a 'six' occurs on one-sixth of all rolls. On a single future roll, 'one-sixth' is a measure of how likely it is that a six will occur, i.e. more likely not to occur.
   (b) 90% of all invoices are paid within 30 days. 90% is a measure of how likely it is that a single future invoice will be paid within 30 days, i.e. very likely.
   (c) No pigs fly. A pig is certain not to fly.
2. (a) $p = 2/6 = 1/3$
   (b) An experiment is required. $p = r/n$ where r occurrences are observed on n trials.
   (c) Make a guess, but do not guess 0 or 1.
4. 40,320
5. (a) 1/6840 (b) 1/1140
6. 5,245,786 ways. Every time we choose six numbers to 'take away', we are choosing 36 numbers to 'leave behind', and so the answers are the same.
7. ^nP_n means the number of ways of arranging n things, taken from among n things, i.e. all n things are arranged. But this is the definition of $n!$
8. To take n things from among n things, you have to take them all; you have no choice. There is only one way to do it, hence $^nC_n = 1$

Answers 2.2

1. (a) 1/26 (b) 5/26 (c) 6/26
2. (a) 1/2 (b) 1/6 (c) 1/12 (d) 7/12
3. (a) 1/36 (b) 25/36 (c) 5/36 (d) 11/36 (e) 10/36
4. (a) 1/8 (b) 7/8
5. (a) 28% (b) 18% (c) 42% (d) 12% (e) 82%
6. (a) 1/5245786 (b) 216/5245786 (c) 9450/5245786 (d) 11900/5245786

Answers 2.3

1. (a) 0.874552
   (b) 0.764841
   (c) 0.015737
   (d) 0.984263
   (e) 0.944516
2. (a) 0.6840 and 0.9001
   (b) 0.948024
   (c) 0.8208
   (d) 0.9859449
3. 0.24225

Answers 3.1

1. (a) 0.5 (b) 0.8413 (c) 0.1587 (d) 0.6826 (e) 0.9182 (f) 0.1116 (g) 0.0477 (h) 0.9974 (i) 0.9500
2. (a) 0.1587 (b) 0.6247 (c) 0.7734 (d) 0.1314 or 0.1292 (e) 0.8643 (f) 0.7605 (g) 0.0968 (h) 0.5 (i) 0 (j) 0.0994
3. 0.9986
4. 32.32% small, 47.06% medium, 14.88% large, 5.74% other.

Answers 3.2

1. Q, R, U and Z only.
2. 0.0625 + 0.25 + 0.375 + 0.25 + 0.0625 = 1, because it is certain (**p** = 1) that the number of heads will be 0 or 1 or 2 or 3 or 4.
3. (a) 0.9838 (b) 0.0162
4. (a) 0.0305 (b) 0.0023 (c) 0.9977 (d) 0.9672 (e) 0.0328
5. 0.9664
6. 0.1314

Answers 3.3

1. N, O, R, S and T only.
2. (a) 0.30% (b) 98.62%
3. (a) 67.03% (b) 32.17% (c) 0.80%

Answers 4.1

1. Between 7.478 and 8.278
2. Between 12.010 and 12.098
3. Between 6.7 and 17.3
4. Between 2.84 and 3.09
5. Between 24% and 36%
6. Between 13.7% and 19.5%

Answers 4.2

1. 79
2. 139
3. 97
4. 733

Answers 4.3

1. 0.410
2. Between 0.017 and 0.082
3. Between −15.48 and −1.52
4. Between −7.44 and −5.06
5. Between −6.05 and 5.25
6. Between 0.0402 and 0.1373

Answers 5.1

1. No. Accept H_0, $\mathbf{z} = -1.25$, critical $\mathbf{z} = \pm 1.96$
2. No. Accept H_0, $\mathbf{z} = -0.89$, critical $\mathbf{z} = -1.645$
3. Reject H_0, $\mathbf{t} = -4.24$, critical $\mathbf{t} = \pm 2.365$
4. Yes. Reject H_0, $\mathbf{t} = 3.207$, critical $\mathbf{t} = 2.132$
5. Yes. Reject H_0, $\mathbf{t} = -2.705$, critical $\mathbf{t} = -1.943$
6. Yes. Reject H_0, $\mathbf{z} = -2.427$, critical $\mathbf{z} = -1.645$
7. No. Reject H_0, $\mathbf{z} = -2.12$, critical $\mathbf{z} = \pm 1.96$

Answers 5.2

1. Yes. Reject H_0, $\mathbf{t} = -16.69$, critical $\mathbf{t} = -2.353$
2. No. Accept H_0, $\mathbf{t} = -0.16$, critical $\mathbf{t} = \pm 2.306$

3. Yes. Reject H_0, Chi-Sq = 40.40, critical Chi-Sq = 3.841
4. Yes. Reject H_0, Chi-Sq = 10.89, critical Chi-Sq = 3.841
5. Yes. Reject H_0, Chi-Sq = 16.28, critical Chi-Sq = 5.991

Answers 5.3

1. Yes. Reject H_0, Chi-Sq = 0.8, critical Chi-Sq = 2.733
2. No. Accept H_0, **F** = 5.33, critical **F** = 6.388
3. No. Accept H_0, **F** = 1.20, critical **F** = 9.01
4. No. Reject H_0, Chi-Sq = 17.55, critical Chi-Sq = 16.919
5. Yes. Accept H_0, Chi-Sq = 4.4, critical Chi-Sq = 11.070
6. No. Reject H_0, Chi-Sq = 2124, critical Chi-Sq = 11.070. After.

Answers 6.1

1. (b) Accept H_0, **F** = 0.58, critical **F** = 5.143. (d) Colour does not affect burning time.
2. (b) Reject H_0, **F** = 27.75, critical **F** = 5.318.
   (d) Clementines are heavier in Tesco.

Answers 6.2

1. The average daily revenue is not the same at all three desks.
2. 'Fats' is the best skate, and Rob is the best skater.
3. When Ahmed uses the 10 ml pipette, he gets an unusually high result. Otherwise all the measurements are rather low.
4. With steel strings, it is quicker to use a plectrum rather than plucking. But with nylon strings, plucking is quicker then using a plectrum.
5. Maggots are better bait than pellets, and the Shannon is better than the Blackwater.

Answers 7.1

1. (a) 98.1% (b) Length = 2.73 + 0.275 Days (c) Beta: Reject. Alpha: Reject. Length is related to days, but is not directly proportional to days. (d) 8.23, PI (7.2890, 9.1710), warning: extrapolation.
2. (a) 98.0% (b) Juice = 25.4 + 0.470 Weight (c) Beta: Reject. Alpha: Accept. Juice is related to weight, and it may be directly proportional to weight. (d) 161.83, PI (126.54, 197.13).

3. (a) 92.9% (b) Food = 55.7 + 8.54 Weight (c) Beta: Reject. Alpha: Reject. Food intake is related to weight, but is not directly proportional to weight. (d) 183.81, PI (124.69, 242.92).

ANSWERS 7.2

1. Forecast = 45.56, i.e. 73.5 − 2.64 × 13 + 6.38
2. Forecast = 16.48, i.e. 16.7 − 0.441 × 13 + 5.51
3. At 5 pm, 33 bookings, i.e. 7.12 + 2.24 × 13 – 3.68
   At 6 pm, 39 bookings, i.e. 7.12 + 2.24 × 14 +0.833
   At 7 pm, 44 bookings, i.e. 7.12 + 2.24 × 15 + 2.846
4. $\mathbf{L_p}$ = 100, 104.20, 110.32. $\mathbf{P_p}$= 100, 103.92, 110.30
   $\mathbf{L_q}$ = 100, 96.38, 107.68. $\mathbf{P_q}$ = 100, 96.12, 107.67
   $\mathbf{F_p}$ = 100, 104.06, 110.31. $\mathbf{F_q}$ = 100, 96.25, 107.68
   $\mathbf{V}$ = 100, 100.16, 118.78
5. $\mathbf{L_p}$ = 100, 107.03, 110.64. $\mathbf{P_p}$ = 100, 105.30, 107.19
   $\mathbf{L_p}$ = 100, 106.02, 114.46. $\mathbf{P_q}$ = 100, 104.32, 110.89
   $\mathbf{F_p}$ = 100, 106.16, 108.90. $\mathbf{F_q}$ = 100, 105.17, 112.66
   $\mathbf{V}$ = 100, 111.65, 122.69
6. $\mathbf{L_p}$ = 100, 107.67, 111.33. $\mathbf{P_p}$ = 100, 106.92, 110.31
   $\mathbf{L_q}$ = 100, 100.00, 94.00. $\mathbf{P_q}$ = 100, 99.30, 93.13
   $\mathbf{F_p}$ = 100, 107.29, 110.82. $\mathbf{F_q}$ = 100, 99.65, 93.57
   $\mathbf{V}$ = 100, 106.92, 103.69
7. National: 100.00, 103.15, 113.67, 119.84
   Regional: 127.50, 128.26, 122.02, 118.41. No, it's falling behind.

ANSWERS 7.3

1. Shrinkage = 0.538 + 0.874 × Square Root Minutes
   Point estimate 2.85, 95% CI (2.69, 3.02)
2. Age, i.e. just one predictor variable.
3. Not useful ($\mathbf{p}$ = 0.151).

ANSWERS 8.1

1. 1.51

ANSWERS 8.2

1. Individuals chart: LCL = 39.77, UCL = 51.89

Xbar chart: LCL = 43.12, UCL = 48.54

3. **np** chart: UCL = 13.1, LCL = 0, because −1.1 makes no sense.
4. **c** chart: LCL = 0.5, UCL = 19.5

Answers 8.3

1. **n** = 68, **Ac** 3, **Re** 4 (alpha = beta = 5% approx)
2. **n** = 94, **Ac** 8, **Re** 9 (alpha = beta = 5% approx)
3. (a) 12.25% (b) 5.50% (c) 32.70% (d) 90.71% (e) 5.2%

Answers 8.4

1. Average bias = −2.6, %Linearity = −5.5%
2. SNR = 5.7, %R&R = 25%
3. Repeatability (row 3), reproducibility (row 2), bias (row 5).

Appendix 2
ADDITIONAL READING AND WEBSITES

Support Material on the Web

http://www.gillmacmillan.ie

On this website you can find a complete set of teaching slides based on this book, all the data sets in electronic format, tips on how to use different statistical software packages, and more.

http://www.minitab.co.uk

From here you can download a fully functioning copy of Minitab statistical software for a free 30-day evaluation, including technical support.

General Reference

Snedecor, G.W. & Cochran, W.G., "*Statistical Methods*", 8th edition, Iowa State University Press, 1989.

This classic is highly recommended and readable, using examples from biology and agriculture. It may be the only other statistical reference book you will ever need. It has about 500 pages and a comprehensive index.

Specific Application Areas

Business

Keller, G., "*Statistics for Management and Economics*", 7th edition, Duxbury, 2005.

This is a large and comprehensive book, but it presents the material simply. It is well laid out and has lots of case studies. It provides worked examples by hand and using software.

Manufacturing

DeVor, R., Chang, T. and Sutherland, J., "*Statistical Quality Design and Control*", Macmillan, 1992.

This is a substantial work on the role of statistics in the design and production processes, with some very good material on experimental design. It is made readable and relevant by setting the techniques firmly in the context of the 'overarching principles' and goals of these processes.

Processes

Oakland, J.S., "*Statistical Process Control*", 5th edition, Harcourt, 2003.
This is a readable book with plenty of examples. It sets SPC in the wider context of organisational philosophy and systems. It provides guidance for the implementation of SPC and process-improvement techniques, including 'six sigma'.

Specific Statistical Topics

Books that focus on a single topic are more challenging to read, but they can be useful for answering specific queries. These authors are all highly regarded.

Sampling

Kish, L., "*Survey Sampling*", Wiley, 1995.
This is an established and authoritative reference book on sampling. It deals with a comprehensive range of issues, including biases, optimum allocation in stratified sampling, economic considerations, geographical issues and other problems.

Attributes

Agresti, A., "*Introduction to Categorical Data Analysis*", Wiley, 1996.
If the sections on contingency tables and logistic regression have given you an appetite for more, this book provides a comprehensive treatment.

Time Series

Chatfield, C., "*The Analysis of Time Series: An Introduction*", 6th edition, Chapman & Hall, 2003.
This book takes the topic to a considerable depth, but Chatfield's style is quite accessible.

Appendix 3

STATISTICAL TABLES

Statistical Table 1

Normal Distribution: Cumulative Probability

z	0.00	0.01	0.02	0.03	0.04	0.05	0.06	0.07	0.08	0.09
0.0	0.5000	0.5040	0.5080	0.5120	0.5160	0.5199	0.5239	0.5279	0.5319	0.5359
0.1	0.5398	0.5438	0.5478	0.5517	0.5557	0.5596	0.5636	0.5675	0.5714	0.5753
0.2	0.5793	0.5832	0.5871	0.5910	0.5948	0.5987	0.6026	0.6064	0.6103	0.6141
0.3	0.6179	0.6217	0.6255	0.6293	0.6331	0.6368	0.6406	0.6443	0.6480	0.6517
0.4	0.6554	0.6591	0.6628	0.6664	0.6700	0.6736	0.6772	0.6808	0.6844	0.6879
0.5	0.6915	0.6950	0.6985	0.7019	0.7054	0.7088	0.7123	0.7157	0.7190	0.7224
0.6	0.7257	0.7291	0.7324	0.7357	0.7389	0.7422	0.7454	0.7486	0.7517	0.7549
0.7	0.7580	0.7611	0.7642	0.7673	0.7704	0.7734	0.7764	0.7794	0.7823	0.7852
0.8	0.7881	0.7910	0.7939	0.7967	0.7995	0.8023	0.8051	0.8079	0.8106	0.8133
0.9	0.8159	0.8186	0.8212	0.8238	0.8264	0.8289	0.8315	0.8340	0.8365	0.8389
1.0	0.8413	0.8438	0.8461	0.8485	0.8508	0.8531	0.8554	0.8577	0.8599	0.8621
1.1	0.8643	0.8665	0.8686	0.8708	0.8729	0.8749	0.8770	0.8790	0.8810	0.8830
1.2	0.8849	0.8869	0.8888	0.8907	0.8925	0.8944	0.8962	0.8980	0.8997	0.9015
1.3	0.9032	0.9049	0.9066	0.9082	0.9099	0.9115	0.9131	0.9147	0.9162	0.9177
1.4	0.9192	0.9207	0.9222	0.9236	0.9251	0.9265	0.9279	0.9292	0.9306	0.9319
1.5	0.9332	0.9345	0.9357	0.9370	0.9382	0.9394	0.9406	0.9418	0.9429	0.9441
1.6	0.9452	0.9463	0.9474	0.9484	0.9495	0.9505	0.9515	0.9525	0.9535	0.9545
1.7	0.9554	0.9564	0.9573	0.9582	0.9591	0.9599	0.9608	0.9616	0.9625	0.9633
1.8	0.9641	0.9649	0.9656	0.9664	0.9671	0.9678	0.9686	0.9693	0.9699	0.9706
1.9	0.9713	0.9719	0.9726	0.9732	0.9738	0.9744	0.9750	0.9756	0.9761	0.9767
2.0	0.9772	0.9778	0.9783	0.9788	0.9793	0.9798	0.9803	0.9808	0.9812	0.9817
2.1	0.9821	0.9826	0.9830	0.9834	0.9838	0.9842	0.9846	0.9850	0.9854	0.9857
2.2	0.9861	0.9864	0.9868	0.9871	0.9875	0.9878	0.9881	0.9884	0.9887	0.9890
2.3	0.9893	0.9896	0.9898	0.9901	0.9904	0.9906	0.9909	0.9911	0.9913	0.9916
2.4	0.9918	0.9920	0.9922	0.9925	0.9927	0.9929	0.9931	0.9932	0.9934	0.9936
2.5	0.9938	0.9940	0.9941	0.9943	0.9945	0.9946	0.9948	0.9949	0.9951	0.9952
2.6	0.9953	0.9955	0.9956	0.9957	0.9959	0.9960	0.9961	0.9962	0.9963	0.9964
2.7	0.9965	0.9966	0.9967	0.9968	0.9969	0.9970	0.9971	0.9972	0.9973	0.9974
2.8	0.9974	0.9975	0.9976	0.9977	0.9977	0.9978	0.9979	0.9979	0.9980	0.9981
2.9	0.9981	0.9982	0.9983	0.9983	0.9984	0.9984	0.9985	0.9985	0.9986	0.9986
3.0	0.9987	0.9987	0.9987	0.9988	0.9988	0.9989	0.9989	0.9989	0.9990	0.9990
3.1	0.9990	0.9991	0.9991	0.9991	0.9992	0.9992	0.9992	0.9992	0.9993	0.9993
3.2	0.9993	0.9993	0.9994	0.9994	0.9994	0.9994	0.9994	0.9995	0.9995	0.9995
3.3	0.9995	0.9995	0.9996	0.9996	0.9996	0.9996	0.9996	0.9996	0.9996	0.9997
3.4	0.9997	0.9997	0.9997	0.9997	0.9997	0.9997	0.9997	0.9997	0.9997	0.9998
3.5	0.9998	0.9998	0.9998	0.9998	0.9998	0.9998	0.9998	0.9998	0.9998	0.9998
3.6	0.9998	0.9998	0.9999	0.9999	0.9999	0.9999	0.9999	0.9999	0.9999	0.9999

The table on p.170 provides the majority probability corresponding to any **z**-score, either positive or negative. To obtain the minority probability, subtract the tabulated value from one.

STATISTICAL TABLE 2

5% Points of the t-distribution

df	One-tailed	Two-tailed
1	6.314	12.706
2	2.920	4.303
3	2.353	3.182
4	2.132	2.776
5	2.015	2.571
6	1.943	2.447
7	1.895	2.365
8	1.860	2.306
9	1.833	2.262
10	1.812	2.228
11	1.796	2.201
12	1.782	2.179
13	1.771	2.160
14	1.761	2.145
15	1.753	2.132
16	1.746	2.120
17	1.740	2.110
18	1.734	2.101
19	1.729	2.093
20	1.725	2.086
21	1.721	2.080
22	1.717	2.074
23	1.714	2.069
24	1.711	2.064
25	1.708	2.060
26	1.706	2.056
27	1.703	2.052
28	1.701	2.048
29	1.699	2.045
30	1.697	2.042
40	1.684	2.021
60	1.671	2.000
120	1.658	1.980
z	**1.645**	**1.960**

$\mathbf{z} = \mathbf{t}_{\infty}$

One-tailed values can be positive or negative. Two-tailed values are positive and negative.

Statistical Table 3

Upper Percentage Points of the Chi-Square Distribution

df	97.5%	95.0%	5.0%	2.5%
1	0.001	0.004	3.841	5.024
2	0.051	0.103	5.991	7.378
3	0.216	0.352	7.815	9.348
4	0.484	0.711	9.488	11.143
5	0.831	1.146	11.070	12.833
6	1.237	1.635	12.592	14.449
7	1.690	2.167	14.067	16.013
8	2.180	2.733	15.507	17.535
9	2.700	3.325	16.919	19.023
10	3.247	3.940	18.307	20.483
11	3.816	4.575	19.675	21.920
12	4.404	5.226	21.026	23.337
13	5.009	5.892	22.362	24.736
14	5.629	6.571	23.685	26.119
15	6.262	7.261	24.996	27.488
16	6.908	7.962	26.296	28.845
17	7.564	8.672	27.587	30.191
18	8.231	9.391	28.869	31.526
19	8.907	10.117	30.143	32.852
20	9.591	10.851	31.410	34.170
21	10.283	11.591	32.671	35.479
22	10.982	12.338	33.924	36.781
23	11.689	13.091	35.172	38.076
24	12.401	13.848	36.415	39.364
25	13.120	14.611	37.653	40.647
26	13.844	15.379	38.885	41.923
27	14.573	16.151	40.113	43.195
28	15.308	16.928	41.337	44.461
29	16.047	17.708	42.557	45.722
30	16.791	18.493	43.773	46.979
49	31.555	33.930	66.339	70.222
50	32.357	34.764	67.505	71.420
99	73.361	77.046	123.225	128.422
100	74.222	77.929	124.342	129.561
119	90.700	94.811	145.461	151.084
120	91.573	95.705	146.567	152.211
149	117.098	121.787	178.485	184.687
150	117.985	122.692	179.581	185.800

Statistical Table 4

Upper 5% Points of the F-Distribution

df	1	2	3	4	5
1	161.4	199.5	215.7	224.6	230.2
2	18.51	19.00	19.16	19.25	19.30
3	10.13	9.55	9.28	9.12	9.01
4	7.709	6.944	6.591	6.388	6.256
5	6.608	5.786	5.409	5.192	5.050
6	5.987	5.143	4.757	4.534	4.387
7	5.591	4.737	4.347	4.120	3.972
8	5.318	4.459	4.066	3.838	3.687
9	5.117	4.256	3.863	3.633	3.482
10	4.965	4.103	3.708	3.478	3.326
11	4.844	3.982	3.587	3.357	3.204
12	4.747	3.885	3.490	3.259	3.106
13	4.667	3.806	3.411	3.179	3.025
14	4.600	3.739	3.344	3.112	2.958
15	4.543	3.682	3.287	3.056	2.901
16	4.494	3.634	3.239	3.007	2.852
17	4.451	3.592	3.197	2.965	2.810
18	4.414	3.555	3.160	2.928	2.773
19	4.381	3.522	3.127	2.895	2.740
20	4.351	3.493	3.098	2.866	2.711
21	4.325	3.467	3.072	2.840	2.685
22	4.301	3.443	3.049	2.817	2.661
23	4.279	3.422	3.028	2.796	2.640
24	4.260	3.403	3.009	2.776	2.621
25	4.242	3.385	2.991	2.759	2.603
26	4.225	3.369	2.975	2.743	2.587
27	4.210	3.354	2.960	2.728	2.572
28	4.196	3.340	2.947	2.714	2.558
29	4.183	3.328	2.934	2.701	2.545
30	4.171	3.316	2.922	2.690	2.534

The top row represents the numerator degrees of freedom, and the left column represents the denominator degrees of freedom.

Index